"Love! What do you know about love?"

"You seem to have some idea that all I ever wanted was to hustle you into bed! Hasn't it ever occurred to you that I like being with you?"

"And bed has nothing to do with it?"

"Well, even if it does, don't you find that even mildly flattering? What is it *you* want, Stacey?"

"I want you to get out of my apartment!"

Rosemary Hammond grew up in California, but has since lived in several other states. Rosemary and her husband have traveled extensively throughout the United States, Mexico, the Caribbean and Canada, both with and without their two sons. She enjoys gardening, music and needlework, but her greatest pleasure has always been reading. She started writing romances because she enjoyed them, but also because the mechanics of fiction fascinated her and she thought it might be something she could do.

Books by Rosemary Hammond

HARLEQUIN ROMANCE
3357—ALL IT TAKES IS LOVE

Playing for
Keeps
Rosemary Hammond

Harlequin Books

TORONTO • NEW YORK • LONDON
AMSTERDAM • PARIS • SYDNEY • HAMBURG
STOCKHOLM • ATHENS • TOKYO • MILAN
MADRID • WARSAW • BUDAPEST • AUCKLAND

ISBN 0-373-17271-0

PLAYING FOR KEEPS

First North American Publication 1996.

Printed in U.S.A.

CHAPTER ONE

STACEY was awakened out of a deep, dreamless sleep by the shrill ringing of the alarm on her bedside table. Groggily she opened one eye. Seven o'clock, and it was still pitch-dark outside. For a brief moment she considered staying in the warm bed and just not going to work today, but, since she was only on temporary status at the advertising agency, a day off would mean a day's less pay.

It had been almost midnight when she'd let herself into her cold, dark apartment, still damp and musty after two weeks without any human occupation. After the emotional farewells with her parents, the long wait for the Boston-New York shuttle, the slow—and hideously expensive—cab-ride from LaGuardia into Manhattan, all she could think of was throwing off her clothes and falling into bed.

Now, even after a quick shower, her head still felt as though it was stuffed with cotton wool. What she needed was a good, strong shot of caffeine. She pulled on a robe and slippers and went into the tiny kitchen to make coffee, but as she scanned the virtually empty food cupboard it dawned on her that she'd run out the day she left for Boston, thinking she'd replenish her supply on the way home.

Groping far in the back of the bottom shelf, she did come across an old jar of instant, kept only for dire emergency since she couldn't stand the stuff, but

it must have been there for years, and when she finally
pried the lid off, there was only a thin dusting of
granules stuck to the bottom.

'Damn!' she muttered, tossing the useless jar into
the trash.

Then she brightened. Hannah! Hannah, her gen-
erous, good-hearted neighbor across the hall! She had
to get up early too, and always kept her cupboards
well-stocked.

She padded to the front door, unbolted it, then
stuck her head out and peered up and down the corridor. Still in her robe, her damp, uncombed honey-
blonde hair pinned up on top of her head, her face
totally devoid of make-up, she didn't want to run into
any of the other tenants. But it was quiet as the grave,
and blessedly empty.

Cautiously she stepped out into the corridor, then
skittered across to Hannah's door. She rapped lightly
on it, then stood breathlessly waiting for several seconds. It was freezing out there, and she tied the thin
robe more tightly around her waist.

When a good half-minute passed with no answer,
she rapped again, more loudly this time. She was
shivering by now, her teeth chattering. After another
long wait, she was just about to give up and go back
into her own apartment when she heard footsteps on
the other side coming toward the door, which pre-
sently opened a crack.

'Hannah,' Stacey called in a low voice. 'It's only
me. Stacey. I just got back last night and I'm out
of——'

She broke off abruptly as the door opened wider,
and she found herself gazing up into the sapphire-

blue eyes of a very tall, very angry-looking man. His raven-black hair was tousled, as though he'd just got out of bed, and his wide thin mouth was turned down at the corners in an expression of intense distaste.

Flustered, she scanned him more closely. What she saw was not reassuring. He was barefoot and dressed only in a pair of worn blue jeans, which had obviously been pulled on quite hastily, since the top button wasn't even done up. With his knuckles resting on his lean hips, his long legs spread apart and a dark morning stubble on his face, he presented a decidedly menacing figure so early in the day.

'Well?' he snarled, in a low, hostile tone. 'What is it?'

For a moment, all she could do was stare up at him, aghast. His bare chest was smooth and well-muscled, with only a thin line of coarse black hair running down the middle until it disappeared under the low-slung waistband of his jeans.

'You're not Hannah,' she finally managed to croak.

'Obviously,' was the dry reply.

Their eyes locked together, and if looks could have killed, she'd have been lying dead at his feet. She clapped a hand over her mouth and started backing away, too stunned to utter another word. But as she watched the angry blue eyes began to soften imperceptibly, then dropped lower in a long, lazy scrutiny. A knowing smile began to curl on the thin lips, and two heavy dark eyebrows were raised in frank appraisal.

It was then she came to her senses and realized what she must look like with her thin, clinging robe, mussed hair and slippered feet. She clutched wildly at the loose openings of the robe, although she had the dismal feeling she was a little late, since he'd already had an eyeful of what cleavage there was to be seen.

She gave the apparition one last horrified look, then, with a little cry, she whirled around, turned tail and ran as fast as she could go back to her own apartment. However, when she reached her door, she found it had quietly shut of its own accord. It always had had that tendency—the building seemed to be settling or something—but in the two weeks she'd been away the problem had obviously escalated.

She grabbed the handle and twisted it, hoping against hope that the lock hadn't caught, but to no avail. It was locked tight. And, of course, she didn't have her key with her.

She stood there shivering, as much from panic as the cold, stunned into immobility and staring blankly at the solidly shut door. Now what was she going to do? The only thing she could think of was to wake up the super and have him come up and use his master key to let her in, a prospect she wasn't looking forward to considering the way she was dressed, not to mention his surly disposition.

In her distress over her predicament, she'd almost forgotten about the man in Hannah's apartment. Could he still be there? That was all she needed—a witness. She prayed he'd gone back inside. On the other hand, he might be able to help her. Men were supposed to be good about things like picking locks.

She turned her head slowly and saw that he was still standing there, his dark head cocked to one side, an amused grin curling on his mouth.

She gave him a shaky smile. 'Uh, I seem to have locked myself out.'

He crossed his arms over his chest. 'So I see.'

'I don't suppose you could...'

He heaved a heartfelt sigh. 'Just a minute.'

He turned and went back inside, leaving the door open. Stacey stretched her neck to peek inside. She couldn't see much, but one thing was clear. All Hannah's familiar furniture was missing.

He came back shortly, brushed past her, and got down on his haunches in front of her door. She stood over him, watching, while he slid what looked like a plastic credit card between the door and the frame. It only took him a few seconds to get it open, but in that short time her eyes became glued to the broad expanse of bare back, the muscles rippling under the smooth skin as he worked, the tousled black hair curling at the nape of his neck.

'There,' he said, pushing the door open and rising so abruptly to his feet he almost knocked her over. 'So much for these modern toy locks. I hope you've got a solid bolt on the other side.'

She cleared her throat. 'Yes, I do,' she managed to squeak.

He was staring down at her, his arms folded across his chest, that same maddening smile on his face. The sapphire eyes were full of amusement, with more than a hint of appreciation in them for what was clearly revealed by the loose robe.

'That's quite a fetching outfit you have on,' he drawled. 'Do you usually run around the halls dressed like that?'

Her face went up in flame. 'I-I already told you,' she began to stammer, 'I-I thought...' Then it dawned on her that he was playing with her, having fun at her expense, and she clamped her mouth shut.

'I know,' he said. 'You thought I was Hannah, whoever she might be. I can understand that. It'd be an easy mistake to make.'

She drew herself up to her full five feet seven, still clutching her robe together, and gave him a lofty look down her nose. 'Tell me,' she said, in her most saccharine tone, 'are you always this clever and amusing so early in the morning?'

The only effect this seemed to have on him was to broaden the grin. 'I think it's always a special occasion when a man and a woman, both half-dressed, meet like this.' He nodded gravely. 'I think it must be fate.'

'Oh, please!' she cried with feeling, waving an arm in the air. 'Spare me your feeble humor. It's too early in the morning.'

She realized then that her dramatic gesture had loosened her hold on the robe, and it was now gaping open. She made a grab at it, but it was already too late. The blue eyes, glinting now in frank appreciation, were sweeping over her again.

He put a finger to his lips. 'Shh,' he whispered. 'Don't want to wake up the neighbors and have them find us out here together, as though we'd just got out of bed. They might get the wrong idea.'

Just then it dawned on her that the door was slowly closing again of its own accord directly behind him. She didn't want to have to go through all *that* again with this aggravating man. She swished past him, nose in the air, stepped inside, then turned to give him one last withering look.

'Thank you very much for your help,' she said stiffly. 'And I'm sorry to have troubled you.'

Without waiting for a reply, she closed the door quietly, locked and bolted it securely, then leaned back against it, her eyes squeezed tight, her heart still thudding painfully. She didn't need this so early in the morning her first day back!

The burning question was, who was that man? He could be a burglar for all she knew. He certainly knew how to get inside a locked door!

She realized instantly how idiotic that idea was. A burglar would hardly have answered her knock in the first place! What, then? Since Hannah was a stout, motherly woman of some fifty-odd years, he could hardly be an overnight guest. And since she was also a spinster, it couldn't be a grown son staying with her. Besides, from the glimpse she'd had inside the apartment, all her things were gone.

The time! What time was it? Glancing down at her watch, she saw that if she didn't get cracking she'd miss her bus. She flew down the short hall to her bedroom to get ready for work. The coffee would have to wait.

After sneaking out of her apartment like a criminal, praying the man wouldn't emerge, she ran past his door to the elevator at the end of the hall, punched the button frantically, then stepped into the car with a sigh of relief when it finally appeared.

When she got off the bus on Madison Avenue, she did manage to gulp down a quick cup of coffee at the espresso bar in front of her office building, and felt marginally better when she stepped into the posh reception room of the advertising agency where she worked as a temporary secretary to one of the account executives.

'Well, good morning, Stacey,' the red-haired receptionist called to her as she passed by the front desk. 'How was the vacation?'

Stacey gave her a smile and a wave and shrugged her shoulders. 'Oh, you know how it is, Dottie. Families!'

The girl rolled her eyes. 'Don't I ever! Anyway, welcome back.' She gave her a knowing look. 'Poor Richard has been chomping at the bit ever since you left. I think he missed you.'

Stacey only smiled and hurried down the long corridor to her desk, just outside Richard's office. She shrugged off her coat, removed the cover from her typewriter, and began to glance through the accumulation of files and memos on her desk.

'Stacey,' said a familiar voice.

She looked up to see her boss, Richard Corbett, just coming toward her from his office, a warm, welcoming smile lighting up his pleasant face. He was a stocky, well-built man of thirty-five, good-looking in a rather colorless way, with curly light brown hair and deeper brown eyes.

'Good morning, Richard.'

He came up to her and took her hands in his. 'How was the vacation?'

'Oh, it was all right. Mother and Dad are inclined to fuss over me, but they mean well.'

'It's really great to have you back. I've missed you.'

She laughed. 'Well, I won't say it's great to *be* back.' Then, when she saw his face fall, she added hastily, 'I don't mean that personally, of course, Richard. I just meant that it's going to be hard to get back into the rat-race again after two weeks of doing nothing but lying around being waited on hand and foot.'

His hands tightened on hers. 'You know quite well, Stacey,' he said in a low-pitched voice, 'that you can change all that any time you're so inclined.'

She gave another nervous laugh and gently pulled her hands away from his. 'Oh, you know how it is, Richard. I've got my own plans right now, and I've worked too hard to give them up.'

He nodded. 'I understand. I told you I wouldn't push, and I mean to keep my word.' Then he brightened. 'But at least have dinner with me tonight. I want to hear all about Boston. It's one of my favorite cities.'

'Oh, Richard, I'm afraid I can't tonight. I just got back late last night and haven't even had a chance to unpack yet. I also have absolutely nothing to eat in the house, not even enough for a cup of coffee this morning, and I need to restock my cupboards.'

'I understand. Tomorrow night, then?'

'Sorry. I have a class tomorrow night.'

He gave a heartfelt sigh. 'You're harder to pin down than the President! When *can* I see you, then?'

She thought a minute. What with holding down a job and going to school at night to get her teacher's certificate, she seemed to be on a constant merry-go-round of frantic activity. She had hardly a moment even to think about a social life, much less the romance Richard wanted. Still, she liked him a lot; he'd been very good to her in the year she'd worked for him. Without the flexible hours he allowed her she could never have juggled job and school.

'Well, how about Saturday night? That would give me the day to get organized at home and the rest of the weekend to relax in.'

'All right. Saturday night it is.' He turned to the pile of paperwork on her desk. 'Now, if you're ready to start, I need to dictate a memo on my advertising campaign for the new breakfast cereal account.'

It had seemed like the longest day of Stacey's life, but it finally did end. She stopped by the corner grocery store on her way home and bought as much as she could safely carry, then walked the half-block to her apartment building.

In the lobby, she stopped to pick up her mail from her box, which was crammed full with two weeks' worth, most of it junk. As she was relocking her box she glanced over at number twelve-G, which was Hannah's apartment. The same card was in the slot, but Hannah's name had been crossed out, a slashing black line through it. Under it, in the same black ink, was scrawled the name 'A. Devereux'.

So Hannah had moved out while she'd been gone. She wondered why she hadn't mentioned it before she left. They'd grown quite close in the several months they'd been neighbors, and Stacey was a little hurt that the older woman had simply moved out without letting her know.

She was alone in the elevator riding up, and as the car went past the twelve floors below hers she leaned back against the wall wearily and closed her eyes. It was at times like these that she was most tempted to take Richard up on his repeated offers of marriage. It would be so nice just to relax and let someone else take care of her. As the wife of an affluent advertising executive, there would be no need to work or go to school.

And she'd finally be able to have the children she'd always wanted. The children she and David, her dead husband, had kept postponing while he got established in his medical practice. Then had come the accident. He was gone, and it was too late. Richard would make a fine father.

There was only one problem. She didn't love him.

Once inside her apartment, she kicked off her shoes and padded into the kitchen to make tea. After her first day back at work and the morning trauma with the locked door, reaction was beginning to set in. A wave of exhaustion passed over her.

She set the kettle on the stove to boil while she put away the few groceries she'd bought—including coffee—and when she was done carried a cup of strong, sweet tea into the living-room, where she sank down on the sofa and took a few tentative sips of the scalding liquid. Setting the cup down on the table to cool, she laid her head back and closed her eyes, bone-tired, every muscle aching.

She caught herself just as she was drifting off to sleep. Snapping her eyes open, she sat bolt upright and reached for the tea. It was cooler now, and she took a long swallow and immediately felt better.

As she set her cup back down her eye was caught by the stack of mail she'd picked up in the lobby lying on the table, and she began to sort through it. Two weeks' worth, and none of it worth waiting for! Junk mail, mostly; a few bills, and, at the bottom, a letter from the company that managed her apartment building, no doubt informing her they'd finally received permission to raise the rent.

She made a face and tossed it aside. She'd deal with it after she'd had something to eat. She got up from the couch, stretched widely, and carried her cup back into the kitchen, draining the now tepid tea on the way. She was just pouring herself a refill when the telephone on the kitchen counter rang.

She snatched it up. 'Hello.'

'Stacey? It's Hannah.'

'Hannah!' she cried, slowly lowering herself on to the stool. 'What in the world has happened to you?'

'Oh, I moved out just a few days after you left for your vacation.'

'Kind of sudden, wasn't it?' Stacey said, hurt. 'I mean, you could have let me know before I left.'

'Sorry about that, Stacey, but I didn't know myself I was leaving until the night before. Luckily a friend of mine was looking for a roommate, and I couldn't turn it down. And I would have called you sooner, but with all the fuss about moving I couldn't remember when you were coming home.'

'I just got back last night.' She laughed. 'You wouldn't believe what a shock it was when I knocked on your door this morning and this strange man—half-naked and very angry—answered the door.'

Hannah giggled. 'My, that sounds interesting.'

'Interesting is hardly the word I'd use. We almost came to blows. But who in the world is he? Did you sub-let or something?'

'I haven't the faintest idea who the new tenant is. I'm only surprised anyone would take the place after what's happened.'

A little shiver of alarm ran up Stacey's spine. 'Just why *did* you move so suddenly?' she asked in a tight voice.

'You know. It's all spelled out in that letter we got from the management company. Oh, I forgot, you just got back last night. Maybe you haven't even read your mail yet.'

'Not really. I just now glanced through it.' From Hannah's tone, it sounded as though her worst fears were going to be realized. 'Oh, Lord,' she groaned, 'I was afraid of that the minute I saw the envelope. I haven't read it yet, but let me guess. They've managed to weasel out of the rent-control and are doubling it.'

'Worse,' Hannah pronounced ominously.

'What could be worse?'

There was a long pause. 'Maybe you'd better read it yourself,' Hannah said at last. 'I hate to be the bearer of such awful news.'

By now Stacey was growing seriously alarmed. 'You'd better tell me now, Hannah. I won't faint.'

There was dead silence on the line for a few seconds, then came the breathless reply. 'They're converting the building to condominiums.'

For a moment, Stacey couldn't quite take it in. Then, when it dawned on her what that meant, it seemed her whole world began to fall apart. She'd *counted* on that low rent to see her through her schooling.

'Oh, no!' she wailed. 'They can't do that!'

'I'm afraid they can.'

'But that means—what exactly *does* it mean? Will we have to buy our apartments?'

'Or get out,' was the firm reply. 'Listen, Stacey, you'd better read the letter yourself. It's all spelled out. Then call me back and we'll talk it over.'

After hanging up, Stacey stumbled blindly back into the living-room to retrieve the letter. Tearing it open, she glanced through it hurriedly, then sank down on the sofa and re-read it more carefully.

When she'd finished, she let it slip through her fingers to fall on the floor at her feet. Although it was couched in barely comprehensible legalese, with complicated juggling of figures, the one thing that she understood perfectly was that somehow, if she wanted to keep her apartment, she'd have to come up with a sum of money that was so far out of her reach it might as well have been millions.

Her new predicament preyed constantly on Stacey's mind. However, the very next day, she received notice that there was to be a tenants' meeting on Sunday afternoon to discuss the situation, and that gave her some relief. Surely someone would come up with a solution.

In the meantime she had a job to go to and classes to attend, not to mention the papers she had to write for school, and was kept so busy she didn't have time to worry. She was also counting on the meeting on Sunday to clarify the situation.

She wondered if the new tenant across the hall would be there. She hadn't seen him again. After talking to Hannah, she was more curious than ever about him. How could anyone be so stupid as to rent an apartment that was shortly going to be converted to a condominium?

She hadn't mentioned the subject yet to Richard. He'd been so busy with the new breakfast cereal account they'd hardly had a moment to discuss anything else. She respected his business acumen, however, and planned to thrash it out with him on their dinner-date, Saturday night.

On Wednesday Stacey had an afternoon class and didn't go in to the office. It rained all that morning, and she seized the opportunity to get some long-neglected chores done. Her hair needed washing, the laundry was piling up, and the apartment needed a good cleaning.

After putting on her oldest faded dungarees and a shabby T-shirt, and tying a scarf over her head, she started out that morning by gathering up the trash that had been accumulating forever. Then, lugging two heavy plastics sacks full of old newspapers, junk mail, and empty jars and cans, she went out into the hall to carry them to the trash bins in the basement.

Just at that moment, the door of the apartment across the hall opened and a tall black-haired figure of a man, dressed in a dark suit, stepped out into the hall.

Oh, no, she groaned inwardly. Not again! Quickly, she turned her head away and stood there rigidly for a moment, gazing fixedly down at the floor, willing him to leave, hardly daring to breathe.

'Good morning,' came a pleasant baritone voice. 'When you're through with that apartment, could you find time to turn mine out?'

Stacey's mouth fell open. He thought she was the cleaning-woman! Obviously he didn't recognize her from their encounter on Monday morning. But wasn't that just as well?

'Sorry, sir,' she muttered, putting on her best Brooklyn accent. 'I ain't got time today.'

His eyes narrowed at her, whether from annoyance at her refusal to clean his apartment or dawning recognition Stacey couldn't begin to fathom. Nor did it matter at that point. Gathering up her plastic sacks, she turned and trudged away from him, her head bent, her shoulders hunched forward, and made for the service elevator.

Blessedly, it wasn't in use and stood there, its doors open, ready to embrace her. She dragged her sacks inside, punched the button for the basement, and breathed a heartfelt sigh of relief as the doors slowly closed before her eyes.

Why, oh, why, she groaned to herself as the ponderous elevator lurched slowly downward, do I have to keep running into the man this way? And why does it bother me so much? What do I care what he thinks of me? Then her eyes widened in dawning awareness as a mental picture of the tall man flashed into her mind, first the disheveled, barely-dressed apparition that had answered the door on Monday morning, then, today, impeccably turned out vision of male perfection she'd just witnessed.

Could it be she was attracted to him? Then she laughed out loud. Possibly, but one thing was certain. There was no way he'd think of her as a desirable woman after the appearances she had put in for him so far.

On her way home from class early that evening, she stopped by the grocery store again to replenish her dwindling supply of food. This time she bought a little more than she had realized, and ended up with two large bulging sacks she could scarcely carry comfortably.

As she trudged down the corridor to her apartment they were getting heavier and heavier, and she just barely managed by shifting them in her arms constantly in an effort to lighten the burden.

It wasn't until she'd reached her door and was trying to juggle the groceries and fish her keys out of her handbag at the same time that she remembered her previous encounters with the man across the hall. Her heart gave a panicky leap and she glanced over her shoulder at his door.

There was no sign of life, but she wasn't taking any chances. The last thing she wanted was to run into that—that *person*—again after his mistaking her for the cleaning-woman this morning. Spurred on by her haste to get inside, she dug deeper for her keys. In the process, she miscalculated the balance of the groceries, and one of the sacks came crashing down on the floor.

Cursing under her breath, she finally did find the keys and got the door unlocked. She set the bag that was still intact inside, then got down on her knees to retrieve the scattered remains of the other one, at the same time awkwardly propping the door open with her foot so she wouldn't have to unlock it again.

She stared bleakly down at the mess, then hastily gathered up several loose potatoes and a soggy egg carton, which even now was dripping from the bottom that had been broken in the fall, sending up a devout prayer of thanks that at least the milk carton hadn't exploded.

She was still scrambling around on the floor, and was about to congratulate herself on managing to clean up the worst of it unobserved, when she heard the door to the apartment across the hall being unlocked. Her heart stopped. Oh, no! It couldn't be! Please, she prayed silently, don't let it be him!

She didn't dare turn around to find out. By now the door had opened and shut, and, by glancing out of the corner of her eye, she could just make out a rather large pair of well-polished cordovan loafers and the cuff of a pair of dark trousers.

'Locked out again?' came a depressingly familiar voice.

'No!' she snapped.

She glanced up at him, and at the sight of him she was literally rendered speechless. Another transformation! Gone was the rumpled, half-dressed, rather sinister apparition that had come to her rescue on Monday morning, and the dark-suited perfection of this morning. There now appeared a clean-shaven man wearing dark gray flannel trousers, a pale blue shirt, crimson tie, and a beautifully-tailored herringbone tweed jacket.

'It looks as though you could use some more help, however,' he said, squatting down beside her.

'No, thank you,' she said, turning back to the mess on the floor. The last thing she wanted was to have this impressive-looking man rooting around among the soggy cartons and scattered vegetables lying at her feet. There was even, in plain sight, a humiliating tub of the richest—and most expensive—brand of ice-cream on the market. And Double Chocolate Decadence, to boot—her one secret indulgence!

Ignoring her completely, he deftly began to retrieve the remaining groceries and replaced them in the sack. When he came to the ice-cream, he turned to her, grinning wickedly. He didn't say a word, but the slashing line of heavy dark eyebrows lifted meaningfully.

In all the confusion, of course, her foot had come away from the door. Flushing hotly, she rose to her feet and unlocked it again, then took the torn sack full of decimated groceries from him and set it down inside. By now, the whole scenario had taken on a slapstick quality, and she gave him a reluctant smile.

'Thank you again,' she said. Then she had to laugh. 'I don't usually make a habit of spilling my groceries all over the hall—or locking myself out of my apartment. Call it culture-shock. I just got back Sunday night from two weeks' vacation.' She hesitated a moment, then held out a hand. 'Since it looks as though we're going to be neighbors, I'd better introduce myself. I'm Stacey Sinclair.'

'Tony Devereux,' he murmured, flashing her a great smile and taking her hand in his. He gave it a token shake, but seemed unwilling to part with it immediately. His own hand was quite large and pleasantly warm, and Stacey herself was reluctant to break the connection.

'You must have moved in while I was gone,' she said pleasantly, drawing her hand out of his at last.

The smile faded. 'Yes,' was the curt reply. 'Now, if you're sure you can manage on your own, I must be off.'

'Oh, yes, of course,' she replied hastily. 'And thanks again.'

'My pleasure,' he said with a brief nod. Then he turned and strode off down the hall toward the elevator.

Tony Devereux, she thought dreamily. He was obviously on his way to an important date, so well-dressed, and she had visions of seductive actresses, gorgeous models. A very attractive man! But rather mysterious. For all the warm smile and playful repartee, there was definitely a cold glint in those blue eyes, and he'd certainly clammed up in a hurry at the first hint of a personal question.

Still, after getting off to a bad start with him, he seemed friendly enough, and he had really been a godsend in getting her door open that first morning. Then today he had even helped with the groceries.

She *wished* he hadn't spotted that ice-cream!

CHAPTER TWO

ALTHOUGH Stacey wasn't exactly on pins and needles with breathless anticipation over her dinner-date with Richard on Saturday night, as she might have been at a more romantic prospect, she was looking forward to it. Besides, at this point in her life, the last thing she was looking for was romance. She'd made her plans carefully, and, if her hectic life didn't kill her, she should end up with that teaching certificate in another year.

It had been a long, gruelling week. After two weeks of pampering by her parents, with nothing to do but loll around and get waited on, it had taken a valiant effort of will to settle back into her normal busy routine, where she had no one but herself to depend on for anything.

A man of solid, predictable habits, Richard always took her to the same restaurant for dinner—a very posh and expensive one, to be sure, the same one where he wined and dined his clients. Although it had become somewhat monotonous by now, the food was wonderful, the service excellent, and Richard, as one of their best customers, was always treated with deference.

In the past, the only really pressing problems she'd had to face was deciding what to wear. She owned exactly two dresses that did justice to the luxurious ambience of the place, both of which she'd practically worn to shreds. Tonight, however, would be the perfect opportunity to wear the beautiful dress her parents had given her for Christmas.

She'd spent a wickedly lazy day, getting up past nine, having a leisurely breakfast and reading the morning paper. Since she'd cleaned the apartment so thoroughly on Wednesday, all she had to do was wash out the few dishes she used and pick up the usual chaos in the living-room before Richard came.

After an hour spent typing up her school notes, she just lounged around for the rest of the day, reading, manicuring her nails and taking a nap until it was time to get ready, assuaging the occasional stab of guilt she felt for her idleness with virtuous thoughts of the past gruelling week.

The new dress was a lovely shade of forest-green that brought out the greenish highlights in her hazel eyes. It was made of a tissue-thin wool crêpe, with long, tight sleeves that buttoned at the wrist and a deeply-cut square neckline that just skimmed the tops of her high, full breasts. It also fit like a dream.

She'd brushed her honey-blonde hair until it shone, pinned it up into a high chignon, made up her face carefully and clipped a pair of heavy gold loops in her ears. She was just about to fasten a thin gold chain around her neck when the front doorbell rang.

Hastily slipping on a pair of high-heeled black pumps, she started down the hall to answer it, glancing at her watch on the way. It was only half-past seven. Richard wasn't due until eight o'clock. Although he was always prompt, he'd never shown up quite this early.

But it wasn't Richard. When she opened the door, there was her new neighbor, Tony Devereux, standing on the other side. For a moment he didn't say a word, only stood there staring fixedly at her, the sapphire eyes alight and traveling over her with obvious appreciation.

'You look...' He smiled and shrugged his broad shoulders, hesitating for a moment. 'Different,' he finally added.

A sensation of intense satisfaction ran through her. For the first time since they'd met she was looking her best. Not in her robe begging coffee, or dressed like a drudge lugging sacks of trash, or frazzled from a hectic work-day, but clearly like a woman even Tony Devereux found worth a second look.

He himself looked marvelous in a formal black dinner-jacket and white tie. His thick dark hair had been recently cut, his jaw was scraped clean of any trace of stubble, and the suit fit his lean muscular frame to perfection.

'I'm sorry to bother you,' he said more abruptly. 'But my telephone seems to be out of order, and I have a rather important call I need to make. I wonder if I could use yours.'

'Of course,' she said, opening the door wider for him. She smiled up at him as he stepped inside. 'I guess I owe you one for disturbing you on my early-morning coffee-hunt.'

'You're obviously just going out,' he commented, with another sweeping appraisal. 'I won't be long.'

'There's no hurry. Come on. The telephone is in the kitchen.'

She started to lead the way into the kitchen, but when he made no move to follow her, she turned back to him with an inquiring look. His hand was on his smooth-shaven jaw, rubbing it thoughtfully, an odd light in the brilliant blue eyes, a half-smile curling his lips.

'Pretty heavy date, I take it,' he said at last. He gestured with one hand, waving it expressively toward her. 'I mean, it must be something pretty important. You look absolutely dazzling in that great dress.' He cocked an eyebrow. 'Fits well, too.'

She flushed, flattered, but a little nervous over his frank appreciation. 'Well, a dinner-date, yes,' she hedged.

The blue gaze swept over her, and she colored even more deeply under his silent scrutiny, fighting down the urge to cross her arms over that low neckline.

'Lucky guy,' he murmured.

She didn't know how to reply to that, but an intense warmth began to steal over her. She was so flustered by now that, before she knew it, she'd dropped the gold chain she'd been carrying.

Immediately he bent over to retrieve it, and held it up, dangling, in his hand. 'Pretty,' she said. 'Is it the fashion now to carry these in your hand rather than wear them around your neck?'

'No, of course not,' she replied tartly, reaching out for it. 'I was just putting it on when the doorbell rang, and . . .'

'Allow me,' he said, taking a step toward her.

She put a hand to her throat and gave him a wide-eyed look. 'No,' she said hastily. 'No, thank you. I'll do it myself.'

He was standing so close to her now that she could smell the distinctly masculine aftershave, see how the tiny lines crinkled at the corners of those amazing eyes, the sweep of the black lashes on his high, prominent cheekbones.

'But I'd like to,' he insisted. 'Come on, turn around. I promise it won't hurt a bit and it'll all be over in a second.'

'You sound like my dentist,' she muttered.

He threw back his head and laughed. 'All right,' he said finally. 'If it makes you feel any better, I don't care if you pretend I'm your dentist. Just turn around, will you, so I can get the thing fastened?'

With a sigh of resignation, she turned her back to him and bent her head. Richard was due any moment now, and she wanted to get Tony Devereux out of there before he showed up. The whole thing would indeed be over far more quickly if she let him do it than if she stood here arguing with him all night.

From the moment she felt his fingers fumbling at the back of her neck, an odd sensation began to steal over her. Little chills began to run up and down her spine, and as the seconds ticked by that sensation grew, until she felt rather light-headed. His hands were warm, his touch light, but when one finger strayed down the contours of her bare back, she came to her senses with an abrupt jolt.

'What's taking you so long?' she demanded, twisting her head around to face him.

'Sorry,' he replied with a grin. 'This clasp is tough to work. It's so damned small. Let me take a closer look.'

As he bent his head and she could feel his warm breath on the back of her neck her heart began to flutter erratically. She knew right then that it was time to put a stop to this nonsense.

'Here, I'll do it,' she said stiffly.

'Never mind. I've got it now.'

'Fine. Now, I'll show you to the telephone.'

Thank God, she breathed silently as she led him into the kitchen, she'd at least straightened up the place that day. She pointed to the telephone sitting on the counter.

'Thanks,' he said. He picked up the receiver and started to dial. 'I won't be long.'

'Oh, take your time,' she said sarcastically as she moved toward the door.

She closed it firmly behind her to give him some privacy, then went back to her bedroom to get her coat and bag. When she gave herself one last glance in the mirror, she couldn't help feeling a little thrill of satisfaction over the obvious impact her appearance had made on Tony Devereux. He was an arrogant, overbearing, even insolent man. But what a man!

She suddenly stopped short and realized where her errant thoughts had been taking her ever since his arrival at her door—thoughts that had threatened to escalate almost out of control during the gold chain episode.

What did she care what the man thought of her? Why was it so important that he was impressed with her appearance, or even that the apartment was clean, for that matter? So he was a great-looking man with a very compelling and seductive air about him. He meant nothing to her. She didn't have to prove anything to him. What was more, that kind of man always spelled trouble. She was behaving like a star-struck schoolgirl.

Still, without thinking, she did dash on a touch more of the rich flowery scent she used for special occasions before gathering up her things and starting back into the living-room.

On the way the doorbell rang again. Richard! She'd almost forgotten about Richard! Right on time, as always. She ran to the door, then, still a little flustered from her encounter with Tony, took a deep breath, smoothed down the skirt of her dress and opened it to him.

'Hello, Richard,' she said with a smile. 'Come on in.'

Watching him as he moved past her, she couldn't help comparing him to the man in the kitchen. Richard was by any standards a good-looking man, a successful man, but something was missing. There was a devilish quality in Tony, a hidden flame, flashing sparks out of those startling blue eyes. He intimidated her, even frightened her a little, the way he simply took over, and in spite of the polished exterior, there was an untamed quality about him that Richard, for all his virtues, lacked.

But Richard was safe, and who needed fire? A man like Tony Devereux only spelled trouble.

She had closed the door behind Richard, and when she turned to him, he was gazing at her in open admiration.

'You look positively gorgeous tonight, Stacey,' he said, moving toward her and taking her hands in his.

She dipped a mock curtsy. 'Why, thank you, sir.'

His hands tightened on hers, and he drew her closer. 'Stacey,' he began in a low voice.

But just then the kitchen door burst open and Tony stepped into the room. Startled, Richard swiveled around and stared, then turned back to Stacey, a bewildered look on his face.

'Uh, Richard, this is Tony Devereux,' she hastened to explain. 'He's my new neighbor. He just moved in across the hall to Hannah's old apartment. He came to use the telephone.'

She glanced at the tall dark man, who was still standing by the door, resplendent in his evening clothes, dominating the room with his presence.

'Tony, this is Richard Corbett.'

He came walking toward them in long, slow strides, his hand outstretched. 'Nice to meet you, Corbett. Stacey very kindly let me use her telephone. Mine seems to be out of order.'

Richard, his eyes wary, his expression guarded, only mumbled a polite 'Devereux' and the two men shook hands briefly. Stacey watched from the sidelines, her heart fluttering, her nerves on edge. Somehow she sensed trouble in the chance encounter, at the least a serious misunderstanding, and what she wanted most at that point was for Tony to leave so she could explain his presence more thoroughly to Richard in private.

'Going out on the town tonight, are we?' Tony asked.

The tone was pleasant enough, but there was an unmistakable note of condescension about it, and Stacey bridled.

'Yes,' she snapped. 'We are. And if we don't hurry, we'll be late for our dinner reservation.' She turned to Richard, who was still staring at the other man through narrowed, suspicious eyes.

'Right,' Tony said in a brisk, cheery voice. 'Well, nice to have met you, Corbett.' He gave him a little salute, then stopped for a moment as he passed by Stacey on his way to the door. 'Thank you again, Stacey,' he said in a deep intimate tone. 'And I'll probably be seeing you later.'

Stacey opened her mouth, then snapped it shut and glared up at him. He was baiting her! Trying to make it appear to poor Richard that they were on much closer terms than was actually the case. But why? Pure devilment, of course! That was the kind of man he was.

She turned from him, then marched stiffly to the door and flung it open. 'Goodnight, Tony,' she said in a curt voice.

He was grinning broadly as he ambled slowly toward her, his even white teeth flashing against the smooth tan of his face, his eyes alight with amusement. As he came closer her eyes widened with apprehension. He was capable of anything.

However, all he did was grin and give her a slight nod as he passed by. When he was safely gone, she turned back to Richard, all ready to do some heavy explaining.

'Richard,' she began.

But she stopped short when she saw the glazed look in his eyes. He simply stood there staring at the door for a few long seconds, then slowly turned to face her.

'Do you know who that man is?' he asked in a hushed voice.

'Yes, of course. He's only a neighbor. I hardly know him.'

'Anthony Devereux,' he breathed, as though he hadn't even heard her.

'Well, yes, I do know his name,' she replied tartly. 'I introduced you, remember?' What was wrong with the man? She gave him a closer look. 'Just who do you think he is?'

He came walking slowly toward her, as though in a trance. 'He happens to be one of the top men at Global Enterprises, which, in case you didn't know, is the city's second largest corporate entity—a real giant.' His forehead creased in a puzzled frown. 'And he lives here? In this building?'

Thunderstruck by the revelation, she only nodded wordlessly.

'That's not possible,' he stated flatly. Then he snorted. 'A Park Avenue penthouse is more like it.'

'Well, you must have made a mistake, then. There may be a hundred Anthony Devereuxes in New York. Why, for all I know he's a plumber. A shoe-salesman. He couldn't possibly be your Tony Devereux. I mean, did you recognize his face or something?'

'No,' he replied slowly. 'I've never seen a photograph of him.' He laughed and gave himself a little shake. 'I don't know, somehow he just *looks* like the Tony Devereux I had in mind. But you're right. I'm probably mistaken. Now, are you all set? Our reservation is for eight-thirty and we're already late.'

'Yes,' she murmured, still a little off-balance. 'I'll just go get my things.'

* * *

On the drive to the restaurant, Stacey's mind kept returning to that odd conversation with Richard about Tony's identity. He was right about one thing; the man did look more like a captain of industry than he did a plumber. But appearances were deceiving. And what did a plumber look like, anyway? You couldn't pigeonhole people that way. Better just forget it. She had more important things on her mind than the true identity of her mysterious new neighbor.

They ate at their usual restaurant, a place of quiet elegance where Richard was well-known, the service and food wonderful, the other diners dressed to the teeth.

'So,' he said, when they'd finished their steaks, 'how is the schoolwork progressing?'

'Oh, pretty well,' she replied. 'It's kind of hard to get back in the swing of it after two weeks away. I have a term paper due next week for my Child Psychology class that I haven't even started yet, but——'

She broke off suddenly when it dawned on her that he wasn't really listening to her. She'd noticed over dinner that he'd seemed abstracted, as though his mind were a million miles away. Clearly he was listening to her now as she rambled on about her schoolwork with only half an ear, which was unusual for him.

'Richard,' she said, eyeing him closely, 'is something wrong?'

He gave her a blank look. 'What did you say?'

'I asked you if something was wrong. You haven't heard a word I've said all evening.'

'Sorry,' he muttered, shamefaced. 'I was just thinking.'

'Well, I gathered that much,' she said with a smile. 'What is it? Problems at the office?'

He waved a hand in the air. 'Oh, no. Nothing like that.' He hesitated for a moment, gazing down at his empty plate, then raised his eyes to hers again. 'I was only wondering about this new neighbor of yours.' He stopped short.

'Yes?' she prodded. 'What about him?'

'Well, if he's the Tony Devereux I think he might be, he has quite a reputation around town as far as women are concerned.' He reddened slightly. 'You know, a different one every few weeks. Affairs that run hot and heavy, then peter out when he loses interest.'

She gave him a puzzled frown. 'So? I don't see what that has to do with me.'

His eyes narrowed at her. 'Don't you?'

'Of course not.' She sighed. 'Richard, he only came to use the telephone.'

He leaned across the table toward her. 'Oh, really? I saw the way he was looking at you in that dress. You may not realize this, Stacey, but, when you take the trouble, you're a very desirable, very beautiful woman.'

She had to smile. 'Richard, I may seem like a babe in the woods to you, but I've been married and widowed, for heaven's sake, and I've been on my own for quite some time now. I'm not a young girl. You don't have to warn me about the big bad predators out there in the jungle.'

'But they *are* there,' he insisted, in a dead serious voice. 'And they don't wear signs warning women like you away from them.'

She laughed lightly. 'Well, I've run across a few of them myself.' Then she went on in more sober tone. 'I don't think you have to worry about me, Richard. I can take care of myself. Besides, Tony Devereux— whoever he might be—doesn't interest me in the slightest. He's an arrogant, boorish, overbearing man, and there's not the least danger in the world that I'd ever fall for his brand of seduction.'

Richard's face brightened. 'Well, that's all right, then.' He reached across the table to cover her hand with his and gave it a little squeeze. 'You've set my mind at rest. For a minute there, back at your place, I had the feeling——' He broke off and gave an embarrassed shrug.

'What?' she asked, curious.

'Oh, I don't know. Just my imagination, I suppose.' He gave her a direct look. 'Only it seemed to me there was something between you, some kind of attraction or understanding.'

She shook her head vigorously. 'Believe me, Richard, nothing could be farther from the truth.'

He nodded, apparently satisfied. 'I realize, Stacey, that I have no right to play the possessive jealous lover,' he said in a low voice. 'Just be careful, won't you?'

'Oh, you know me,' she replied lightly, 'I always play it safe.'

Later, lying in bed that night after Richard took her home, Stacey's mind wandered back to that conversation. What amazed her most was that Richard, a rather unimaginative, almost stodgy type, had been so sure he'd sensed some subtle nuance between her and Tony Devereux that he'd seen fit to warn her about him.

It was ridiculous, of course, but in her hazy state, just at the edge of sleep, she seemed to feel once again the warmth of his breath on her neck when he had fastened the clasp of her gold chain, the chilling sensation evoked in her by the touch of his hands on her bare skin, to see the agile grace with which he had moved and, not least of all, how outrageously handsome he had looked in his evening clothes, all broad shoulders and slim hips.

Her last thought as she drifted off to sleep was that although she'd convinced Richard she had no interest in the man, she wasn't quite so sure of it herself.

The next day was Sunday. The tenants' meeting to discuss the problem of the condominium conversion was set for three o'clock that afternoon, and Stacey didn't want to miss it.

She spent the entire morning working on the paper for her Child Psychology class, then at two-thirty, after a long leisurely lunch over the enormous Sunday newspaper, she went into her bedroom to get ready to go to the meeting.

She stood before the open closet door debating what to wear for at least ten minutes. A woolen dress was too formal, jeans and a sweatshirt too casual, a suit too businesslike. Finally she realized that time was growing short, and when it dawned on her what she was doing—and why—she grabbed a pair of dark green flannel trousers and a white silk shirt out of the closet and hastily began to throw them on.

What did she care if Tony Devereux showed up at the meeting or not? she grumbled to herself as she combed out her thick tawny hair to her shoulders and applied a dash of pale coral lip-gloss. Then, without another glance in the mirror, she slipped on her most casual flat-heeled shoes, grabbed her handbag and left for the meeting.

On the way way to the elevator, she glanced at the apartment across the hall, but there was no sign of life, and no sound came from inside. Maybe he was already there. She was a little late.

When she arrived at the large recreation room in the basement of the building it was already filled, almost every chair taken. The meeting hadn't started yet, however, and she scanned the crowd, hoping to see someone she knew to sit with. Finally she spotted two other women who lived on her floor. One of them beckoned to her, pointing at the empty chair beside her, and Stacey headed toward them.

Glancing over the crowd on the way, she satisfied herself that Tony Devereux was not among those present. Either he was even later than she was, or he didn't plan to attend at all.

She sat down next to Gladys Farmer, an elderly widow who lived just down the hall from her. 'Thanks for the seat, Gladys,' she said as she settled herself. 'I'm glad to see such a good turn-out.'

'Oh, yes,' the older woman said, with a brisk nod of her white head. 'Everyone is simply up in arms about this affair. Many of us live on fixed incomes and count on the rent-control to keep us here at all.'

'I know,' Stacey replied. 'I'm pretty much in the same boat. There's no way I could come up with the amount they're asking for the down payment if they do convert.'

'Ladies and gentleman, fellow tenants!' came a resounding voice from the small platform at one end of the room. 'Shall we begin our meeting?'

The buzz of conversation gradually subsided and all eyes turned to the portly balding man who had taken charge. Stacey knew him slightly—a retired school principal, who was obviously used to running meetings like this.

'We've arranged to have a few speakers from among the tenants who have researched our situation,' he went on. 'One is a lawyer, the other an employee at the Housing Authority. When they're through with their reports, I'll open the meeting for questions. Now, let me introduce our first speaker.'

At the end of the long, informative, and at times very stormy meeting, Stacey came away convinced of one thing. If she couldn't somehow come up with a sizable sum of money within the next month, she'd better start looking for another place to live.

The telephone was ringing in her apartment when she let herself in. For a moment, she was tempted not to answer it. Thoroughly depressed by what she'd learned at the tenants' meeting, she was in no mood to chat with anyone.

Finally, however, the incessant ring began to get on her nerves. She marched into the kitchen and snatched up the telephone. 'Hello,' she snarled.

'Darling, what's wrong?' came her mother's voice.

Stacey sank down on the stool beside the counter. 'Oh, Mother, I'm sorry. I just found out that I'm going to have to give up my apartment.'

'Oh, no! How awful! Did they manage to find a way to raise the rent?'

'Worse. They're converting to condos, and that means a heavy down payment, not to mention a mortgage I can't afford anyway.'

She hadn't meant to mention the situation to her parents, but her mother had caught her at a weak moment, and she just blurted it out. The minute she did, however, she could have bitten her tongue out. She should have known her mother's first instinct would be to bail her out.

'Well, not to worry, dear. We'll find the money somehow. How much do you need?'

When Stacey mentioned the amount, she could hear the quick intake of breath at the other end of the line. Somehow, saying it out loud to her mother made it sound even more astronomical.

'That's quite a large sum, isn't it?' her mother was saying in a worried voice. 'Let me talk to your father, and we'll call you back when we've come up with a solution.'

'No, Mother,' she stated flatly. 'I'm sorry I mentioned it to you at all. I appreciate the thought, but I've got to handle it myself. In the first place you and Dad don't have that kind of money to throw around, and in the second, if I'm going to stand on my own two feet in this world, I can't go running to you for help every time I get in trouble.'

'But, Stacey——'

'No "buts", Mother,' she broke in firmly. 'I mean it. In fact, I'd rather you didn't even say anything to Dad about it.' Then her voice softened. 'I'm sorry, Mother. I don't mean to sound ungrateful. I really do appreciate your wanting to help, but please try to understand.'

Hoping she'd finally convinced her well-meaning mother that she had to solve her housing problem strictly on her own, she said goodbye.

She had just hung up the receiver when the doorbell rang. Most likely one of the other tenants come to commiserate, she thought, and ran to answer it.

It was another tenant, all right, but not one she'd expected. Tony Devereux stood there, looking like a million dollars in a pair of well-fitting black chinos, a bright blue turtle-necked sweater, obviously cashmere and just the color of his eyes, and a different tweed jacket, also expensive.

'Hi, neighbor,' he said disarmingly, with a flash of white, even teeth.

Stacey, however, was not disarmed. 'What do you want?' she snapped.

'Hey, is that any way to greet a neighbor?' he asked, giving her a hurt look.

But Stacey was in no mood to be cajoled. 'Well?'

'I was just going out for a bite to eat and thought you might like to join me. You know how it is on Sunday evenings.'

Something about his tone annoyed her. It was as though he had turned to her as a last resort to fill in a boring evening.

'Sorry,' she said curtly. 'I have other plans.'

'I see. Going out again with...' He frowned. 'What's his name? Oh, yes, Richard.'

'No,' she snapped. 'I'm not.'

'Someone else, then?'

'No. Not that it's any of your business.'

'Well, then, why not have dinner with me?'

'Because...' She faltered, not exactly sure why, except that something about the arrogant cock of his head, in fact just the way he was standing there, with that aggravating supremely confident air, made her bristle.

'Listen,' she said through her teeth. 'After the show you put on for Richard last night, I wouldn't walk across the street with you.'

'Ah,' he said, nodding owlishly. 'I understand. The boyfriend might object. Is that it?'

'No!' she exclaimed angrily. 'That's not it. In the first place he's not "the boyfriend", and in the second he doesn't care what I do.'

'Then I don't see why...'

Finally she'd had enough badgering. She put her hands on her hips and glared at him. 'You don't *need* to see why, do you? I won't have dinner with you because I don't *want* to have dinner with you. That's all the reason you need. I've had a rotten week, I'll probably lose my apartment, and...'

Suddenly it was all too much for her. She felt the hot tears stinging behind her eyes, heard her voice crack, and then, to her horror, burst into tears.

CHAPTER THREE

SQUEEZING her eyes shut tight, Stacey turned away from him, hoping he wouldn't notice, but of course it was far too late for that. As she struggled for control she heard the door close quietly. Oh, good, she sighed inwardly. He's gone. She could collapse in peace.

She gave a loud sniffle and was just groping in her pocket for a tissue when she suddenly sensed a presence behind her. She raised her head and darted a swift glance behind her.

He hadn't left after all! He was still standing there, just inside the door, staring at her aghast, his face white. The look of helpless horror on it, as though he was totally out of his depth, struck her as so comical that laughter started bubbling up within her, mingling with her tears, and she turned her head quickly away again so he wouldn't notice.

'Hey, now, Stacey,' she heard him mumble. 'Stop that. I didn't mean——' He broke off lamely.

Her whole body was shaking by now, whether from laughter or tears she couldn't quite make out. Then, when she felt a tentative hand come to rest on her shoulder and he started patting her feebly on the back in a fumbling effort to comfort her, she couldn't hold back the giggles a second longer.

As they erupted the hand on her shoulder was dropped immediately. 'Are you laughing at me?' he demanded angrily.

When she finally managed to get herself under control, she wiped her eyes on the back of her sleeve and turned around to face him. His arms were crossed in front of him, his head lowered, and the blue eyes were narrowed at her with the deepest suspicion.

At the sight of him, the laughter threatened to explode again, and she clapped a hand over her mouth. But it was too late. She couldn't help herself. It was really too funny. Here was this supremely confident—not to mention arrogant—man, first reduced to helpless impotence by a woman's tears, and now standing there like a petulant little boy whose favorite toy had just been taken away.

As she struggled to muffle her giggles she sneaked a quick, guilty look at him. He still looked hurt and angry, but she did notice that the corners of his mouth had begun to twitch. His face worked as he made a valiant effort to sustain the frown, but in the next moment he too was chuckling under his breath.

'You little devil,' he said, with a shake of his head.

'I'm sorry, Tony,' she apologized with a sigh. She finally found a tissue in her pocket and blew her nose loudly. 'I couldn't help it. I know you meant well.'

He cocked his head to one side and gave her a sober, enigmatic look. 'Just don't count on that too often,' he said softly.

His tone was light, but there was no mistaking the hard edge to it, and a little thrill of fear went through her. He seemed to be issuing her some kind of warning.

Then he brightened perceptibly. 'In fact, I think you owe me that dinner now, just for putting me on that way.'

'All right,' she agreed, relieved. 'You've got a point. But I'd really rather not go out. I was just going to fix myself a quick tuna casserole and a salad. Not exactly gourmet fare, but you're welcome to share it with me if you like.'

'That sounds great. I haven't had a home-cooked meal for ages.'

'Well, come on into the kitchen, then. You can talk to me while I put it together. I think I might even have a bottle of wine tucked away.'

They went into the tiny kitchen, where she did find a bottle of inexpensive Chardonnay far back in the fridge. She handed it to him, along with a corkscrew and glasses, and while she started in on the casserole, he opened the wine and poured it out.

Although he was such a large man that he domi-nated the small room, she found his presence oddly comforting. The little scene over her tears seemed to have broken down a barrier between them, made her feel more at ease with him. Somehow, seeing him at a disadvantage had made him more approachable, and much more human.

'I didn't see you at the tenants' meeting this afternoon,' she said as she diced onions and celery. 'Surely you know that the owners of the building are threatening to convert all our apartments into condos.'

'Oh, I was there,' he replied. 'I just didn't stay long. The whole thing is a total waste of time.'

She turned around and stared at him. He was sitting at the round table over by the window, leaning back comfortably, his long legs stretched out in front of him, but the blue eyes were cold, the firm jaw hard and set.

'Why do you say that?' she asked carefully.

He shrugged. 'The tenants haven't a prayer of winning. They could all spend their time much more profitably looking for new housing.'

'Then why did you take over Hannah's apartment in the first place? You must have known about it before you moved in. That's why she had to leave.' She laughed dryly. 'Probably why most of us will. In fact, it could mean the end of all my future plans. So you can't blame us for fighting for our homes.' She turned and frowned at him. 'Doesn't it bother you?'

He shrugged. 'Well, one has to live somewhere, and when I heard there was a vacancy here, I just decided to take it. It's a good location, and you'll have to admit the rent you're now paying isn't exactly making a profit for the owners. Somehow I doubt they consider themselves a charitable institution.'

'Yes,' she agreed slowly. 'To be fair, I suppose that's true. They do have their side of it. But then so do we,' she added stoutly. 'A lot of the tenants couldn't come up with the exorbitant down payment they're asking in a million years. Or afford a more expensive apartment, for that matter.'

'That, my dear girl,' he said in a flat tone, 'is what's known as life.'

Stung by his cavalier attitude, she frowned at him. 'That sounds pretty callous.'

He shrugged. 'Possibly. But also true.' Then he smiled. 'But let's not spoil the evening by arguing.' He reached for the wine and refilled his glass. 'I'm much more interested in you and those plans of yours. Tell me about them.'

She had to admit he had a point. An honest difference of opinion didn't have to lead to an argument. And the nice smile did go a long way toward soothing her ruffled feathers.

'Oh, I've been taking education classes at Columbia to get my teaching certificate. And——' she held up two fingers '—I'm that close to it. Another year and I can start teaching.'

'That's great,' he said.

There was a discernible note of surprise in his voice, as though he'd expected something quite different, and she gave him a questioning look.

'You don't sound very convinced,' she remarked lightly, and turned to resume her chopping.

'Well, I was just wondering if that was as far as your dreams went.' His tone was casual, but she sensed an underlying note of disapproval in it.

Her hands stilled on the wooden block. 'For now, yes,' she said evenly. 'Anything wrong with that?'

He raised a hand in the air. 'Of course not,' he replied. 'It's a very worthwhile, very commendable goal.'

She laughed shortly. 'That's the kind of sentence that usually has a "but" tacked on to it.'

She scooped up the vegetables and dropped them into the casserole dish, then mixed in the tuna, Chinese noodles and mushroom soup and put it in the oven.

'There,' she said, setting the timer. 'Half an hour or so should do it.'

She sat down at the table across from him and he topped up her wine-glass. A sudden squall had come up, and it seemed very cozy in the warm kitchen, the raindrops spattering against the window, the barely audible ticking of the oven-timer, the radio playing softly in the background, the pleasant bite of the wine.

Even the silence seemed soothing. There was something very satisfying about cooking for a man again. It had been a long time, not since David was killed. She and Richard always went out to dinner. She'd instinctively shied away from inviting him to a meal, afraid it might seem to him that she was interested in putting their relationship on a more intimate footing.

Yet that factor didn't bother her where Tony Devereux was concerned. But why should it? He was only a neighbor, after all, and certainly wasn't pressing her into romance the way Richard was. There was no reason to be on her guard against him.

She glanced over at him. He was just sitting there, totally at ease, sipping his wine, his brilliant blue eyes darting around the room, taking in every detail.

He really was a remarkably good-looking man, she thought, watching him covertly. His features were finely-chiseled, with a long straight nose, high wide cheekbones, square chin and strong jawline. He also had nice flat ears, a quality that had always appealed to her in a man.

Then, suddenly, his gaze shifted, and before she could look away their eyes locked together for a moment and he gave her a slow smile, almost as though he could read her wayward thoughts.

She flushed a little and said lightly, 'Penny for them.'

'I was just wondering,' he said. 'You seem like such a domestic sort, yet your future plans appear to be centered entirely on the work you want to do and don't include marriage.' He cocked his head to one side, eyeing her closely. 'Somehow I picture you in a vine-covered cottage somewhere in the country, wrapped up in a hard-working husband, with the patter of little feet in the background.'

She took a hurried sip of wine and looked away. 'I've been married,' she said shortly.

'Oh?' was his only comment, after a short hesitation.

'Yes. He was killed.'

'I'm sorry.'

She shrugged. 'Well, so am I, but it happened quite some time ago, and it's true, time really does heal all wounds.'

'Were you happy together?'

She gave him a suspicious look, wondering if he was trying to be flippant, but his expression was serious, even sympathetic.

'Yes,' she replied softly. 'We were. Of course, we were very young.' She laughed. 'And who knows what the future would have had in store for us if he'd lived? I haven't noticed that many happy marriages around these days.'

'Nor have I,' he said soberly. 'One very good reason why it's definitely the single life for me.'

He sounded so positive, almost as though it was a warning, that she was somewhat taken aback. 'That's a pretty flat statement. I take it you've never been married, then?'

He shook his head vigorously. 'No. Not even tempted.' Then his mouth curled in a lazy smile. 'But just because I'm not interested in a permanent commitment doesn't mean I intend to deny myself the company of women, or the pleasures of romance. You sound as though you're giving up the whole ball of wax.'

'Well, let's just say I have more important things on my mind at the moment.'

'Does that include the boyfriend? Richard, was it?'

She colored. 'Richard is not "the boyfriend", as you put it. I work for him. We're friends. That's all.'

He laughed. 'I don't think Richard sees it quite that way.'

'Well, that's Richard's affair, not mine.' She drained her glass and jumped to her feet. 'That casserole will be done soon. I'd better get started on the salad. How do you feel about avocado? A lot of people don't like them.'

'Oh, as far as food is concerned I'm a human garbage-can. I'll eat anything that's put in front of me, especially if it's home-cooked. Except liver,' he amended. 'I can't stand liver.'

'Well, neither can I, so you're safe on that score.' She tossed dressing into the salad and carried it to the table. 'We might as well start with this,' she said, setting it down. 'The casserole should be done by the time we finish.'

'Can I help?' he asked, half rising from his chair.

She motioned him to sit down and took her own chair. 'There's really nothing to do.'

As they ate it dawned on her that although he'd quizzed her about every aspect of her life, he'd actually volunteered very little about his own, nothing, in fact, except that he was apparently a confirmed bachelor.

'You know,' she said with a little laugh, 'I have no idea what you do for a living. You must have a job of some kind.'

'Oh, yes,' he replied. He hesitated for a moment. 'But I'm afraid it's a little difficult to explain.'

'That sounds interesting. And rather ominous. Nothing illegal, I hope.'

He gave a short barking laugh. 'Hardly! Not that I know of, at any rate.' He swallowed his last bite of casserole and leaned back in his chair with a satisfied sigh. 'That was wonderful,' he commented.

She waited him for to go on about his work, and when he didn't say anything she tried again. 'Well? You still haven't told me what it is you do.'

'Didn't I?' He seemed surprised. 'Maybe that's because it's really rather boring. I work for a large corporation that has many interests—various types of investments, mainly in small companies—and I sort of dabble in most of them, check on them from time to time to make sure they're paying their way.'

She frowned. 'You mean, a sort of accountant or auditor?'

'Sort of.'

Then she recalled the conversation she'd had with Richard about him, the possibility that he had some exalted position with a major corporate giant. Since she couldn't recall the name of it, there was no point in asking him.

Besides, it didn't seem likely. If he was Richard's Tony Devereux, he'd never be living in a rent-controlled apartment. And since he wasn't exactly forthcoming about his work, it would probably be best to drop the subject. Whether he was the man Richard thought he might be didn't actually make a whole lot of difference anyway.

Except that she suddenly remembered what Richard had said about Tony Devereux's reputation with women. Now *that* she could believe. Not only because of his great looks and the confident masculine air about him, but also the subtle sexual nuances he'd displayed while he fastened that gold chain around her neck, the way he'd looked at her in her new dress, the hooded blue eyes appraising, as though sizing up her availability.

'Penny for them.'

She looked up to see those same eyes, a dark cobalt now, gazing fixedly at her. She was about to toss off a flip remark about her thoughts not being worth a penny, when something in that look stopped her. It was almost as though he already knew what she'd been thinking and, what was more, as though his mind had been running along the same lines.

While she watched, mesmerized, he rose slowly from his chair and came around to stand behind her. She sat there paralyzed, unable to move, and when his hands came down on her shoulders, she closed her eyes with an inaudible sigh.

The next thing she knew his cheek was against hers, the rough stubble scratching lightly, sensuously, on her skin. She took a deep breath and opened her mouth, but nothing came out. He put a hand on the side of her head, forcing it around slightly so that his mouth met hers, softly, almost playfully, with only the lightest pressure, drawing on her lower lip, holding it gently in his teeth.

Then, as the pressure increased, her head fell back. His mouth opened over hers, and she felt the tip of his tongue seeking entry. At the same time the hands on her shoulders slid lower, hovering for several moments at the opening of her loose silk shirt, his fingers stroking the sensitive skin of her neck, her upper chest, running along the ridge of her collarbone.

It wasn't until one hand slid lower to cover her breast that she came to her senses. She tore her mouth away from his and turned to look at him. The desire burning in his eyes was unmistakable, and she was strongly tempted just to relax and let it happen. But something stopped her. It wasn't just their differences about the proposed condo project that bothered her, but something about the man himself, his secretiveness, his unwillingness to talk about himself.

Hastily she jumped up from her chair. 'I think we'd better call it a day,' she said in a shaky voice. 'I'm a little tired, and, since I have to go to work tomorrow morning, it's probably just as well to make an early night of it.'

He cocked his head at her, and a slow, knowing smile spread across his face. 'Right,' he said, glancing at the thin gold watch on his wrist. 'It probably is time I was on my way.' He gave her a nice smile. 'And I don't want to wear out my welcome right off the bat.'

She walked with him to the door, and when she'd slid the bolt and opened it for him he turned to her. 'Thanks again, Stacey, for the great meal. And the pleasant company.'

So, she thought, gazing up at him, he really was going to leave, just like that. Somehow she'd expected

an argument. There wasn't even going to be any discussion. Here she'd been all primed to beat him off,
and he wasn't even going to keep trying! Maybe he
just didn't think she was worth the effort.

'You're welcome,' she said with a forced smile.
'Half the fun of cooking is sharing it with someone
else.'

'Goodnight, then. I'm sure we'll be seeing each
other.'

With that, he was gone, the door closed behind him.
She could hear his footsteps in the hall, crossing over
to his own apartment, the turn of the lock on his door.
Then silence.

Although she couldn't help feeling a little disap-
pointed, she knew it was probably just as well. He'd
made it crystal-clear that he was not in the market for
a commitment of any kind, so there couldn't possibly
be any kind of future where he was concerned.

But what an adventure it might be!

On Tuesday night there was another tenants' meeting,
just a small group this time, to discuss possible ways
to combat the owners' proposed conversion. They met
in the apartment of Peggy Connors, who lived two
floors below Stacey.

There were only six people present, all representing
different occupations, and all of them violently op-
posed to the conversion plan, but, after two hours of
heated discussion, the general consensus was that they
really didn't have a leg to stand on. This was confirmed by the leader of the group, Jack Gardner, who
was a corporate lawyer and very knowledgeable about
the legalities of their position.

Peggy Connors, who was a schoolteacher, wouldn't accept that conclusion. 'I don't believe it, Jack,' she announced firmly when he'd finished setting forth his depressing conclusion. 'Surely we have some rights, especially those of us who have lived here for several years.'

The others all murmured their agreement. 'I'm afraid it's a fact of big city life,' said Joan Fiorino, who was the gardening editor of a small neighborhood newspaper. 'I see it happening all over town when I go on my interviews.'

Stacey turned to the lawyer. 'Jack, since you're the expert here, I guess we have to take your word for it, but surely there must be some legal recourse.'

Jack, a portly middle-aged man with a head as bald as an egg, gave a helpless shrug. 'The most I can do right now is use every delaying tactic in the book. I won't go into the technicalities, and eventually we're going to lose, there's not a doubt in my mind about that——' he brightened '—but we can give them a hell of a run for their money.'

The meeting broke up shortly after that, and Peggy drew Stacey aside as the others were leaving. 'Stay a minute and have a last cup of coffee with me,' she murmured in her ear.

Stacey nodded. 'Sure,' she replied.

After they'd all left, Peggy, a short redhead about Stacey's age, kicked off her shoes with a sigh of relief and headed for the couch in the living-room. She flopped down on it and poured out their coffee, then turned to Stacey with a rueful smile.

'Depressing, wasn't it?'

'I'm afraid so. It looks like we're stuck.'

'Well, let's not talk about it any more. I'm sick of the whole subject.' She eyed Stacey narrowly. 'At least you've got Richard on the string to turn to.'

Stacey had to laugh. 'Let me tell you something, Peggy,' she stated firmly, 'I've come too far on my own even to consider turning to a man to bail me out at this point.'

'Good for you!' She took a long swallow of coffee, made a face, then set her cup down and leaned her head back on the couch. 'Speaking of men,' she began.

They both laughed at the same time. 'Why is it,' Stacey said, 'that every time women get together they eventually get off on that subject? I wonder if men talk about women that way?'

'I doubt it. They're too egotistical. Anyway, as I was saying, who's that dishy new neighbor of yours?'

'You mean Tony?'

'Ah,' Peggy said, rolling her eyes. 'So it's Tony, is it?'

Stacey colored. 'Well, he only lives across the hall from me.' She gave an offhand shrug. 'You know, I borrowed some coffee one morning, he used my telephone when his was out of order.' She eyed Peggy carefully. 'Why do you ask? Do you know him?'

'No, worse luck! But I'd like to. I've run into him a couple of times in the elevator and passed him in the lobby, but so far he hasn't so much as given me a second look. Any suggestions?'

'Sorry,' Stacey replied, shaking her head. 'As far as I know, he's not interested in that kind of thing.'

'Oh, no!' Peggy groaned. 'Not another gorgeous hunk who turns out to be gay!'

Stacey could feel herself blushing. 'Hardly,' she murmured almost inaudibly, smiling to herself at the outrageous suggestion.

'It's not fair!' Peggy went on. 'The good ones are all either married or don't like women. What's a poor single girl to do?'

Stacey finished the dregs of her coffee and rose to her feet. 'I'm afraid I don't have an answer for that one,' she said with a laugh. 'Except to enjoy our work as much as possible.'

'Well, that's easy for you to say. Wait until you actually have to deal with the little monsters. You'll change your tune.'

'You don't mean that, Peggy. I know you love your work.'

'OK, I admit it.' She grinned. 'But I also love to complain. Come on, I'll see you to the door. And if you get the chance, tell that great-looking new neighbor of yours that there's a very sexy redhead living just two floors below him.'

For the next two weeks Stacey didn't have the chance to put in Peggy's bid, even if she'd had any intention of doing so, because Tony Devereux simply dropped out of sight.

After cooking dinner for him, she'd been almost certain he'd return the favor shortly. After all, the whole thing had come about because he'd asked her out. Had something happened that evening to change his mind? Was he deliberately avoiding her?

No, that made no sense at all. Most likely he'd been at loose ends that evening, and had just wanted someone to share a meal with. It meant nothing. She had her own busy life to lead anyway, and didn't have the time or energy to waste on thoughts of Tony Devereux.

However, she did keep an eye out for him. She would look for him in the lobby or the hallway or elevator, and even on a few occasions stood listening at his door, straining her ears for any sign of life behind it.

In the end, after two weeks of total silence from him, she finally gave up. Maybe he'd even moved out without telling her. But then there was no reason why he should. They hardly knew each other. And there was certainly no room for a man like him in her hectic life, especially if she was going to have to start hunting for a new apartment soon.

So far Jack Gardner's legal delaying tactics, whatever they might be, seemed to have worked—at least for the time being. There were no more letters from the owners, at any rate, and it was already past the time they'd given to respond to their offer to buy. She'd just have to keep her fingers crossed and hope for the best.

It was on a Thursday night, just as she was leaving for her evening class, that she saw Tony again. With her handbag slung over her shoulder, and carrying an armload of books, she had just tested her door to make sure it was locked when she heard the door to the apartment across the hall open.

She turned around to see him standing in the doorway. For a moment they only looked at each other, neither of them saying a word. In the two weeks since she'd seen him she'd almost forgotten how attractive he was, how compelling the tall figure, leaning now against the doorframe, one arm braced against it, how brilliant the sapphire-blue eyes against the deeply-tanned face.

'Oh,' she said at last. 'Hello.'

He came strolling toward her. 'Hello, yourself,' he said, flashing her a wide smile. 'I was just on my way over to see you.' He dropped his gaze. 'Just coming home from school?'

'No,' she replied. 'Just going there, as a matter of fact.' She paused, wishing the sight of him, his nearness, didn't make her heart pound so, or her knees feel so weak. 'Did you want anything special?' She grinned. 'A cup of sugar maybe? Or some coffee?'

'No. I'm not borrowing. I came to ask you to have dinner with me tonight.'

For a split-second, she was tempted to cut her class but, on second thought, knew she couldn't do that. 'Oh, I'm sorry,' she said. 'I can't. I have a class.' She glanced at her watch. 'And if I don't hurry, I'll be late.'

'Don't go,' he said promptly. 'Surely it won't hurt to miss one class.'

She laughed. 'Ah, that's easy for you to say. You already have a good job. I'm still slaving away at that temporary position in Richard's office, and if I don't get this teaching certificate, I'll be there forever.' She gave him a closer look. 'You look as though you've been in the sun. Have you been on holiday?'

'No. I've been working.' He grinned, the even white teeth flashing against his tanned skin. 'It just happened that the small electronics firm I had to visit was located in sunny Florida.'

'Lucky you,' she murmured. 'Now, I really must go.'

She started to move past him, but he held out a hand, stopping her. 'Then I can't talk you into skipping your class and having dinner with me?'

Once again, she was tempted. There was nothing she would have liked better, but she couldn't do it. 'Sorry. I'd like to, but I really can't. Not tonight,' she added.

He frowned briefly, just the hint of a shadow passing over his features, as though he wasn't accustomed to being turned down for any reason at all, much less schoolwork. She had to smile to herself. It wouldn't hurt him to have at least one woman say no to him. That monumental ego could stand it.

'Well, then, how about tomorrow night?' he asked.

She thought for a moment. It would be Friday, and she had no other plans. 'All right.'

'Say, around seven o'clock?'

She nodded. 'That'll be fine.'

'Good. I'll see you then.'

As she started down the hall away from him she was uncomfortably aware that he was still standing there. She could feel those blue, blue eyes boring into her back every step of the way, and was grateful that there was a car waiting for her when she reached the elevator.

The next night he took her to a small, out-of-the-way restaurant that specialized in Vietnamese food, not far from their building. It was an unseasonably balmy night for New York in January, and they decided to walk the few short blocks.

She'd debated endlessly about what to wear. In the end she decided that if he'd meant to take her to someplace elegant he would have mentioned it, so she dressed casually, in a deep rust-colored woolen dress that was rather dated in style, but fit her well and did nice things for her slim figure.

Although Tony wore a white shirt and tie, he too was dressed casually, in dark gray flannel trousers and a navy blue jacket. Stacey was not a small woman, but even in her high-heeled black boots he was still inches taller than she was, and it gave her a heady feeling to be walking down the street with such an attractive man.

In the restaurant, which was quite small and redolent of every kind of exotic food, they were seated in a booth that had high wooden partitions separating it from their neighbors, and the enclosed space made it seem quite cozy, even intimate, though it was a rather noisy place.

She took one look at the complicated menu, and gave Tony a look of dismay. 'I have no idea what any of these things are!' she exclaimed.

'Well, let's have some wine first, shall we? Then I'll translate for you. I've been here many times and sampled most of their food.' He laughed. 'Even so, I'm still not sure what's in most of it. Let me tell you, however, it's all wonderful.'

The wine he ordered was unfamiliar to her, but then she wasn't a connoisseur anyway, so it didn't make much difference. It was light, rather dry, and went down quite easily.

'So,' she said, after he'd ordered and they were sipping their wine, 'tell me about Florida.'

He shrugged. 'There's really not much to tell. Our company owns a small electronics firm just outside Miami. They've been showing a loss for the past six months, so the powers that be sent me down there to try to find out why.'

'And did you?'

'Oh, yes,' he said wryly. 'It didn't take long.'

'What was the reason?'

'Mismanagement,' he stated flatly. 'Pure and simple.'

'What will your company do about it?'

'I don't know. Probably get rid of it.'

'But won't that put a lot of people out of work?'

He gave her a condescending smile. 'Stacey, it's a business we're trying to run, not Neighbors in Need. If we don't show a profit, then *we'd* be bankrupt.'

She shook her head sadly. 'Oh, I know. It's just that—well, the company my Dad worked for was sold out from under them several years ago, and he was without work for months. It was terrible for my mother, too, watching what it did to him. In fact, they never really recovered from it. So, although I understand that, as the saying goes, "Business is business", it still makes me sad to think of people losing their jobs.'

'Well, until someone comes up with a better way to run things, we're stuck with the profit motive.'

His casual acceptance of tragedy in other people's lives made her bristle. 'I'm afraid that's not good enough,' she objected heatedly. 'It may be true in your world, where the almighty dollar is all that matters, but when you're dealing with real human beings with real problems it just won't wash.'

He gazed down his long straight nose at her for a few moments, his eyes hooded, steely. 'And I'm afraid you haven't a clue what you're talking about,' he stated flatly.

'Oh, haven't I?' she challenged, lifting her face to his. 'I saw what those kinds of tactics did to my own father when he was made redundant, and no amount of rationalization about business being business can ever convince me there was any justice to it.' She could hear the tremor in her voice and turned her head away.

In a moment she felt his hand clasp hers. 'Come on, Stacey,' he said softly. 'Let's not argue about something neither one of us can change. And I hate shop-talk on my own time.' He lowered his voice and leaned toward her. 'I missed you while I was away.'

At the touch of his hand, the intimate tone of his voice, Stacey's anger drained away, her heart gave a little flutter, and she raised her eyes to his. 'You did?'

'Oh, yes,' he assured her. 'I'd become accustomed to seeing you out in the hall in your robe, locked out of your apartment, masquerading as the cleaning-woman . . .'

'You knew!' she cried. 'All along you knew that was me!'

He grinned hugely. 'Well, I'm not blind, you know.' His hand tightened around hers. 'And you were certainly the sexiest maid I'd seen in a long time.'

She flushed, deeply gratified at the words. His hand felt very warm, very large, very reassuring, holding hers. Somehow she had the feeling that tonight he wouldn't be as easy to handle as he'd been last time, and she wasn't quite sure what she'd do about it when he did make his move.

A man like Tony Devereux didn't come along often, and when he did, the worst thing a woman could do was fall for his practiced charm, no matter how tempting the prospect might be. Devastating, yes. Immensely appealing, yes. But trustworthy? Not in a million years. And she began gearing herself up mentally to resist the pass she knew was coming later on.

The food arrived just then, and she quickly withdrew her hand.

It was late when they walked back to their building, the streets almost deserted. There had seemed to be endless courses to the wonderful meal, then, after dinner, a small combo arrived and started to play, mostly old popular songs. By the time they'd had coffee and a few leisurely after-dinner drinks, it was past eleven o'clock.

At the door to her apartment he stopped, and waited while she got out her key. Now he'll make his move, she warned herself, and wondered what approach he'd use. Probably the old, Aren't-you-going-to-invite-me-in? routine. Well, forewarned was forearmed, and she wouldn't let him get away with it.

After she'd unlocked the door, she turned to him with a pleasant smile. 'Thank you, Tony, for the enjoyable evening,' she said. 'The dinner was everything you said it would be.'

He braced a hand against the wall and stood gazing down at her, a slow, seductive smile playing about his lips. 'I'm glad,' he said. 'I enjoyed it, too. We'll have to do it again some time.'

Suddenly, before she realized his intention, the dark head dipped down and his cool lips brushed against hers. Then, just as suddenly, he raised up and pushed himself away from the wall.

'Now,' he said, 'I know you've had a long day, so I'll say goodnight.'

It took a heroic effort of will for Stacey to keep her jaw from dropping, her mouth from falling open, and the astonishment from her eyes. The man was a chameleon. Just when she'd been all prepared to thwart him and his bag of tricks, he'd managed to turn the tables on her very neatly.

'Uh, yes,' she stammered. 'Goodnight, then.'

He waited until she'd stepped inside and turned on the light, then, with a little salute, he turned and started toward his own apartment just as the door closed shut.

CHAPTER FOUR

ONCE inside her apartment, Stacey simply stood there with her eyes closed, in a daze, leaning back against the door. Then, as though they had a will of their own, her fingers moved involuntarily to her mouth. She could still feel the feather-light pressure of his lips against hers, taste the wine he had drunk, smell the clean scent of his skin.

He had taken her completely by surprise. All primed to ward off a blatant seduction, that brief, sweet kiss had done far more than any overt pass possibly could have to weaken her defenses and leave her longing for more.

Her eyes flew open. Of course! It was all part of his game-plan! He must have seduction calculated down to a fine art and know quite well just how to get under her skin. Nothing so vulgar as a direct frontal assault. Oh, no! He knew quite well that sneaking in through the back door was the way to her heart.

Still, she had to smile. She was on to his game—and it was just a game to him, she was certain—so why not relax and enjoy it? So long as she knew what to expect she wouldn't be in any danger of falling in love with him. And, when he did make his move, she could stop him whenever she chose to. Assuming, of course, she added to herself, that he gave her the chance.

*   *   *

She didn't see him at all during the following week. Then, late the next Sunday afternoon, he simply appeared at her door again, just as she was finishing up her school assignment and trying to think of what to have for her supper.

When she opened the door and saw him standing there, grinning at her, a familiar little thrill of anticipation ran through her. He was so darned attractive!

'I had a sudden craving for pizza,' he said. 'And thought I might be able to talk you into going out to indulge along with me.'

She frowned down at her faded dungarees and shabby cotton shirt. 'Oh, Tony, I'm not dressed to go out.' She smiled up at him. 'And, to tell you the truth, I don't feel much like changing.'

'Well, then, let's call and order one in,' he replied promptly.

'All right. That sounds great.'

He gave her an exaggerated leer. 'Your place or mine?'

Laughing, she opened the door a little wider to let him in. 'Come on. Better make it here. I think I might even be able to put a salad together.'

When the pizza arrived they sat at her kitchen table, gorging themselves and drinking the beer Tony had brought from his own place. In spite of his supreme self-confidence and obvious sophistication, he was a very comfortable person to be with, and it seemed quite natural to be here with him in her tiny kitchen, dressed in her old shabby clothes.

There had been another tenants' meeting earlier that day, and Stacey had felt obligated to attend, even though the committee was clearly getting nowhere except to delay the inevitable takeover. Still, delay was better than instant eviction, and at this point she'd take what she could get.

'I went to a meeting of our tenants' committee today,' she remarked casually.

'Oh?' he said, reaching for another slice of pizza.

She waited, but when he continued to sit there, contentedly chewing, she bridled. 'Aren't you the least bit interested in the fate of your apartment?'

'Not really,' he remarked with a shrug. 'These things seem to take their inevitable course, I'm afraid, and there's not an awful lot committees and meetings can do about it, except give people the illusion that they're taking some action.'

'That sounds pretty fatalistic,' she said, getting up to pour out the coffee. She set down the cups and took her chair. 'And our delaying tactics do seem to be working, at least for the moment.'

He cocked an eyebrow at her. 'Is that the plan?' He thought a moment, then shook his head. 'You might gain an extra month or two, but in the end you'll have to give in.'

'Well, even if you're right, at least we're trying.'

'And what exactly are you accomplishing?' he asked in a clipped voice.

'We're letting those bandits know we won't give in without a fight,' she replied stoutly.

He shook his head. 'But in the end you *will* give in.'

Although she knew in her heart that he was probably right, she found his uncompromising tone maddening. 'I don't understand you, Tony!' she exclaimed hotly. 'If you're right, you're going to end up losing your apartment just like the rest of us.'

'Oh, I'm right,' he pronounced coldly. 'Make no mistake about that. I just happen to be a realist.'

She jumped to her feet and stood glaring down at him. 'Isn't a realist actually someone who just doesn't care enough about anyone or anything to take a stand?'

He looked up at her, and the icy glint in his eyes gradually seemed to thaw. 'I care,' he said softly. 'But only when I believe there's a chance of getting what I want.'

As Stacey met that blue gaze, saw the tender look on his face, her resolution began to falter. The contradictions in the man kept her continually off-balance. One moment he was like a ruthless machine, consigning hundreds of people to homelessness without a qualm, all in the name of business, and the next he was suddenly transformed into a warm, caring person, a lovable person.

'What *do* you care about, Tony?' she asked quietly, sinking back down in her chair. She propped her elbow on the table, chin in hand, and studied him for a moment. 'You know, it occurs to me that although you like to quiz me about my life, you never talk about yourself.'

A slow smile spread across his face. 'Maybe that's because I lead a very dull life.'

'Oh, come on. I don't believe that for a minute.'

'All right, then, Madam Prosecutor. Fire away. What do you want to know?'

'Oh, just the usual.' She thought a moment. 'For instance, where were you born?'

'Believe it or not, right here in New York City. Grew up here, too. Went to college at Columbia.'

'What about your family?'

'Don't have any,' he replied promptly. 'No brothers, no sisters. Not even a cousin.' He sighed deeply and gave her a look of mock self-pity. 'I'm just a poor orphan.'

She thought about his obviously expensive clothes, the way his time seemed to be pretty much his own. 'Ah, the old rags to riches story,' she said lightly.

He gave an explosive laugh. 'Not exactly. My parents were killed in an automobile accident when I was eighteen, just old enough to be on my own. They very considerately left me with the wherewithal to finish my education and get started in business.'

'Just exactly what *is* your business, Tony?' She laughed. 'You're so vague about it that you make me wonder if you're not some kind of underworld kingpin or criminal mastermind.'

His eyes widened in astonishment, then he laughed again. 'That's some imagination you've got! Although I'll have to admit there are those who might agree with you. But no, my occupation is perfectly legitimate. It only sounds vague because it's a little hard to define exactly.'

It was obvious from his offhand tone that he wasn't going to elaborate, and at this stage in their relationship she didn't feel she should pry too deeply into his affairs. Maybe he was involved in some kind of secret work. A spy, perhaps—FBI or CIA.

Chuckling inwardly at her fanciful imagination, she got up to clear the table, but when she reached in front of him for his plate he put a hand on her arm, stopping her. 'Don't do that now,' he said. 'With your busy schedule I see little enough of you as it is. How about an after-dinner drink first?'

She thought a minute. 'Well, I may have an old bottle of brandy back in the farther reaches of my cupboard, left over from some special occasion I can't even recall, but it's probably ancient.'

'Sounds great. Brandy improves with age.' He rose from the table and raised his arms up, stretching widely. 'Mind if I put on some music?'

The stretching exercise had pulled the sweater he was wearing up from the waistband of his dark trousers to reveal a narrow band of tanned flesh, and for a brief instant she was so mesmerized by the tantalizing sight that she didn't reply. In fact, until he dropped his arms by his sides again, she scarcely heard him.

'No, of course not,' she said quickly, tearing her eyes away. 'Just ignore the mess in the living-room. I've had a busy week and haven't been able to do much cleaning.'

'You have a busy *life*!' he said with a smile.

While she retrieved the brandy and poured it out Tony wandered into the living-room. After a moment she heard the sound of the stereo. He'd found her record collection, and a slow show-tune was playing softly when she joined him.

He was leaning back on the sofa, his arms behind his head, his long legs stretched out in front of him, his eyes closed. She stood in the doorway for a moment looking at him, at his thick dark hair gleaming in the light of the lamp beside him, the way the gray pullover he was wearing clung to his muscular upper body.

He opened his eyes just then and gave her a warm smile. 'Ah, I see you've found the brandy.' He patted the cushion next to him. 'Come and sit beside me.'

She hesitated for a fraction of a second, but in the end knew she wouldn't be able to resist. When she did sit down, his arm came around her, and he drew her head down on his shoulder. They sat in silence for some time, listening to the music, taking an occasional sip of brandy.

Stacey was filled with a deep sense of total contentment, and when his other hand cupped her chin, turning her head so that she was facing him, it seemed the most natural thing in the world for his mouth to come down on hers in a long, tender kiss.

'Mmm,' he murmured. 'You taste good.' He moved his mouth to her hair. 'Smell good, too.'

The arm around her shoulders tightened, he shifted his body around toward her, and once again his lips claimed hers, this time with more urgency. It felt so heavenly that Stacey simply gave herself up to it, and it wasn't until she felt the tip of his tongue pressing against her lips, the hand on her cheek slide down toward the loose opening of her shirt, that she pulled back from him.

'Stacey?' he said. 'What is it?'

'Oh, nothing, really.' She gave a nervous laugh. 'I guess I'm a little worried about moving too fast.' She smiled at him. 'You know, I'm basically a pretty cautious person.'

'Yes,' he commented in a dry tone. 'I'd noticed.' He thought for a moment, then returned her smile.

'Well, I'm not—cautious, that is. But I don't push—or beg—either.'

Before she realized his intention, he'd risen abruptly to his feet. 'Now,' he said, stretching, 'it's probably time I went home.'

Although she hated to see him go, she knew it was probably for the best. What she really needed right about now was some time away from his disturbing presence to try to sort out her thoughts.

'Tony,' she said slowly, rising to stand by his side. 'I hope you understand. I mean . . .'

He put a finger on her lips. 'No need to explain,' he said in a pleasant tone. 'Your standards might be a little rigid for my taste, but there's no hurry. I like you, Stacey. A lot. And I admire you, what you're trying to do with your life. I may want more than that, but for now I'm satisfied just to get to know each other better. All right?'

She nodded happily. 'Yes. That's fine.'

They had reached the door by now. He reached for the handle but, before leaving, his head dipped down again to brush his lips lightly over hers. Then he held her chin in his hand, tilting her head up so that she was gazing into those startling blue eyes.

He gave her a quirky smile. 'But you can't blame me if I keep on trying.'

With that, he was gone.

From that night on, they began to see each other often, sometimes two or three times a week. He soon came to know her busy schedule, and adapted to it without any fuss.

Usually he took her to small, out-of-the-way restaurants for dinner, followed by a movie, which they both enjoyed, and occasionally she would cook dinner for him and they would make an early night of it.

He was unfailingly attentive, an amusing companion who seemed genuinely interested in her life, her plans. He was also an affectionate person, and would take her hand as they walked along the street, put his arm around her waist as she preceded him into a restaurant or cinema, and it did a lot for her ego to see the way other women ogled him wherever they went, their eyes bright with envy.

This went on for about three weeks. Although in all that time the serious pass she was expecting never did materialize, and she never actually felt pushed, his kisses did become more ardent, his hands more venturesome. So she'd managed to keep him at a safe distance, but it was becoming more difficult all the time, and very wearing on her own nerves.

Of course there was no doubt that his one aim was to get her into bed with no commitment. The trouble was that by now she was so attracted to him, so flattered by his attentions, that when his hands began to stray or his kiss became more demanding, she herself longed to throw her innate caution to the winds and enjoy this devastating man to the fullest.

What she feared most, of course, was that once she gave in to him, she'd lose control of the situation, become just another trophy to add to his collection, and she'd lose him in the end anyway. Still, in time it began to seem more and more pointless to resist something they both wanted. She also had a sinking feeling that it was probably inevitable anyway. She was no blushing virgin, after all, and in a few years she'd be thirty. What was she waiting for?

At the end of February the school term ended, giving her a whole week free for the semester break. When she mentioned this to Tony, his eyes lit up immediately.

'Well, we'll have to celebrate, won't we?' They were just finishing dinner in a small Italian restaurant, and chin in hand he thought for a moment, then said, 'I have it. How do you feel about opera?'

'Opera?' she asked, startled. 'I don't know. To tell you the truth, I've never been to one. I'm afraid my musical tastes are pretty simple. How do you feel about it?'

'Oh, I'm an opera maniac.' He laughed. 'Although I should warn you. Once you get hooked, it's like an addiction. You can't get enough of it. I'll tell you what. The Met is putting on a new production of *Carmen* Saturday night. It's a good one to start out on, very accessible. If I can get tickets, that is. How about it?'

By now she would have gone to the moon with him if he'd asked her. 'Why not?' she said with a smile. 'I'll try anything once.'

He reached across the table and took her hand in his. 'Anything?' he asked softly, his eyes glittering at her in the dim light of the restaurant.

She laughed. 'Well, almost. Remember, I'm basically a very cautious person at heart, you know.'

He drew his hand away. 'Yes,' he commented dryly. 'I've come to realize that.' He rose to his feet. 'Shall we go?'

He was silent during the taxi-ride home, sitting over on his side of the seat, chin in hand, gazing out the window. When they reached her door he didn't follow her inside as he usually did, but instead seemed almost anxious to leave.

'By the way,' he said, turning back. 'Saturday is opening night, so it will be pretty dressy. Do me a favor and wear that great green dress of yours.' He placed a hand on her cheek. 'You know, the one that brings out all the green fire in your eyes.'

Then, with a last perfunctory kiss, he turned and left.

Inside her own apartment, the door shut, she stood there listening to his footsteps crossing the hall, feeling a little wistful about his sudden restraint. Had her reserve made him lose interest at last?

Then she gave herself a little shake. If so, it was probably all for the best. He'd made it crystal-clear, right from the start, that he was a footloose man who had no intention of tying himself in any kind of commitment to a woman. She really should be grateful.

On Saturday night Stacey was just putting the finishing touches on her subdued make-up when the doorbell rang. Her heart gave a little leap, and she glanced down at the green dress, smoothing the skirt, adjusting the low neckline, then went to let Tony in.

He looked marvelous, dressed in the same formal dinner-suit he'd had on that first night he'd come to use the telephone, the white shirt dazzling against the tanned skin of his face, the elegant dark suit fitting his tall lean frame to perfection.

'Ah,' he said, standing back, his eyes sweeping over her. 'You did wear it.' He stepped inside and closed the door. 'Even the same gold chain, I see.'

She flushed a little, recalling the night he'd fastened it around her neck. 'Well, it seems to go with the dress.'

He gave her a crooked smile. 'But I wish you'd waited and let me fasten it again,' he said in a low voice. 'Now,' he went on, more briskly, 'if you're ready, shall we go? We don't want to miss the overture on your first night at the opera.'

Although the whole world of opera was a new experience for her, she found the production so lavish, the costumes and the sets so perfect, and enough of the music familiar to her, that she thoroughly enjoyed the whole thing.

Somehow, Tony had managed to come up with some of the best box seats in the house, and although there were six other people sitting in it, all strangers to her and apparently to Tony, too, it seemed like a cozy little world of their own, sitting there close together in the darkness, the gorgeous music soaring over them.

Tony was obviously mesmerized, totally immersed in the drama, the singing, the orchestra. During most of the performance he sat bent forward in his chair, elbows braced on his knees, chin propped in his hands, his eyes glued to the stage.

At one point, however, toward the end of the first act, he leaned back and bent his head to her ear. 'Are you OK?' he asked in a low voice.

'Oh, yes,' she reassured him.

He gave her a brilliant smile and reached over to take her hand, interlacing his fingers with her own. 'Good girl,' he whispered.

During the intermission they wandered out with the crowd to the bar for a glass of wine. Watching him as he stood in the crush of people waiting to be served, she found herself comparing him to the other men there. By any standards he was far and away the most dashing, the most impressive-looking. And he belonged to her! Well, sort of. At least for the moment.

When he finally came back to her, holding two glasses, they started to make their way to a quiet corner where they could drink their wine in peace, but before they'd gone far she heard a man's voice calling Tony's name.

Tony stopped short, frowning, and turned slowly around. 'Oh, hell,' he muttered under his breath.

Looking past him, in the direction of the voice, Stacey saw a small, nondescript man striding purposefully toward them, one hand outstretched, a rather obsequious smile on his face. He gave Stacey a brief, apologetic glance, then turned to Tony.

'Mr Devereux,' he said. 'Am I glad to see you! I've been trying to get hold of you for days.' He sucked in a lungful of air, as though to work up his nerve, then pressed on. 'You know, about that business we discussed last time we met?'

Ignoring the man's hand, Tony gave him that long look down his nose that Stacey had come to recognize as a storm brewing. Standing close beside him, she could feel the tension in his whole body, tell by the rigid way he held himself, the look on his face, that he was barely keeping in check his anger at the un-

welcome interruption, and she steeled herself for a
scene, wishing with all her heart she could just vanish
into thin air until it was over.

'This is hardly the place for business, Pomeroy,'
Tony said in a hard, clipped voice.

The man's face fell, and he dropped his hand to his
side. 'But I haven't been able to get through to you
any other way,' he protested. 'And, as you know, my
situation is becoming desperate. If you'd just give me
ten minutes...'

'Sorry,' Tony said, in a no-nonsense voice that
brooked no refusal. 'Now is neither the time nor the
place.'

'Well, can I make an appointment, then?' the man
pleaded.

'Not with me, you can't. Call my secretary.'

'But I *have* called your secretary, several times in
fact, and I always get the same answer.'

'Then that's the answer you're going to have to live
with,' Tony replied in a tone of utter finality. 'Now,
if you'll excuse me, it's almost time for the second
act.'

Gripping Stacey firmly by the elbow, he simply
turned his back on Mr Pomeroy and walked away.
Although she longed to ask him what it was all about,
she felt certain he wouldn't welcome any prying into
his business affairs, and after seeing that hard, almost
brutal side to him, she didn't want to be on the re-
ceiving end of it.

The five-minute gong rang just then anyway, and
they had to leave their wine half-finished. By the time
they arrived back at their seats, Tony seemed to have

resumed his good humor, the unpleasant little scene apparently forgotten.

He put an arm around her shoulders and bent his head to her ear. 'You're going to love this act,' he whispered.

Just then the conductor appeared at the podium. Tony withdrew his arm from her shoulders and, leaning forward, his eyes gleaming, enthusiastically joined in the burst of applause.

During the entire taxi-ride home, Tony expounded on the production to her. Although most of it was way over her head, it was obviously a subject that was very important to him and one he'd given a lot of thought.

He was still talking as they rode up in the elevator and walked down the corridor to her door, and to-night he automatically followed her inside, as though anxious to finish his lecture. She only half listened to him, still pondering the Pomeroy episode.

Then, just as he was taking off her coat, he stopped in mid-sentence. She turned to give him an inquiring look and saw that he was standing behind her, his face stricken.

'God, what an unholy bore!' he exclaimed, striking his forehead with he palm of his hand. 'Why didn't you shut me up hours ago? You shouldn't let me run on like this.'

'Well, you told me you were an opera maniac. So I was forewarned.' She had to laugh. 'Tony, don't look at me like that. I enjoyed the opera very much, and I want to learn. Now, sit down and I'll fix us a cup of coffee.'

'You're an amazing girl, you know that?' he said.
'With that bottomless fund of tolerance you seem to
have, you'll make a fine teacher.'

Glowing under the compliment, she felt closer to
him at that moment than ever before. So close, in
fact, that she decided to raise a rather touchy subject,
one that had been bothering her ever since the
intermission.

'Tony, who is Mr Pomeroy? And why was he so
upset?'

Immediately the pleasant smile on his face faded.
'It's not important,' he said gruffly. 'The man is a
pest, and should never have tracked me down and
barged into my personal life that way.'

'But who is he?' she persisted. 'He seemed so
desperate.'

Tony waved a hand in the air. 'The world is full of
desperate people, Stacey. I'm not responsible for them
all. If you must know, Pomeroy owned a small automobile parts factory that my company had to shut
down a few months ago.'

'I see. Just like the electronics firm in Florida. And
you? What's your part in all this? Are you the hatchet-
man?'

His face darkened. 'That's not a very pretty way to
put it.'

'No? I'm sorry. But is it true?'

With a resigned sigh, he came over to her, cupped
her chin in his hand and gave her a thin smile. 'I tried
to explain to you once, Stacey,' he began with elaborate patience, 'that there's no room for charity in
business affairs. Sure, people like Pomeroy get hurt.

It's a fact of life. Unpleasant perhaps, but a fact none the less.'

She knew he was probably right, by his lights, but it still bothered her. Where business was concerned he seemed almost inhuman, more like a machine than a living, breathing man. It seemed logical that some of that coldness would spill over into his personal relationships as well.

As if to belie her conclusion, he began to stroke her face. 'Come on, Stacey,' he said in a low voice. 'Let's not spoil a great evening.' He put his hands on her shoulders and stood back, eyeing her appreciatively. 'I was so wrapped up in my opera lecture that I haven't even told you how lovely you look tonight. Or,' he added, his eyes dropping lower, 'what that dress does for me.'

She gave him a searching look. All the hard lines in his face had been smoothed, and what she saw in the blue eyes, gazing intently down at her, made all her reservations about him seem pretty trivial.

They stood there for several moments, neither speaking nor moving. It was almost as though he was waiting for a reaction from her. The trouble was her heart was pounding so hard, her knees felt so weak, and the blood was singing so wildly in her veins that she couldn't think, couldn't speak, couldn't move. All she knew was that this was what she'd been waiting for, that being held in this man's arms was exactly what she wanted at that moment.

He placed a hand under her chin, tilting her face up until their eyes met. Then, slowly, his head bent down toward her. She closed her eyes, and the next thing she knew his warm, soft lips were claiming hers in a deep, sweet kiss that thrilled her to the very depths of her being.

Gradually, the pressure of his mouth increased, the hand on her back pressed her more tightly to him, and the hand cupping her chin moved down to clasp the base of her neck. As his lips parted and she felt the tip of his tongue seeking entry she drew in a sharp breath, and instinctively raised her arms up around his neck.

'Oh, God, Stacey,' he breathed, tearing his mouth from hers at last and pressing it against her ear. 'You'll never know how badly I've wanted to do this, for weeks now.'

She couldn't speak, could barely breathe. As his mouth began to nuzzle along her jaw, her cheek, down to her neck, and his hand to travel over her back, she raked her fingers through the dark hair, which curled slightly at the nape of his neck, crisp and clean under her touch.

His mouth came down on hers again, this time with more urgency, and her lips automatically parted. The hand at her throat slid downwards, hovered for a moment on the bare skin just above the low bodice of her dress, then moved lower until it came to rest on her breast.

As the large warm hand moved across from one full, soft thrusting mound to the other Stacey's head began to whirl. She fought hard to think where all this was leading, but it felt so wonderful, and she'd been without a man's touch for so long, that she felt powerless to stop him.

'I want you, Stacey,' she heard him mutter in her ear.

The hand at her breast slipped underneath the neckline of her dress, his fingers seeking, searching. The hand on her back moved down to clutch at her hips, pulling her up against his lower body so that she became acutely aware of his own hard need.

Then, suddenly, both arms came around her and she felt herself being swooped up into his arms. It wasn't until she realized that he was striding quite purposefully down the hall toward her bedroom that she finally came to her senses. Was she really ready for this? He wanted her; there was no doubt in her mind now about that. But he hadn't spoken one word of love.

'Tony,' she said. 'Please. Put me down.'

They were just outside her bedroom by now, the dim light filtering into the hall from the living-room the only illumination. She looked up at him. Even in the shadows she could make out the puzzled look on his face. Slowly he eased her down, until she stood on her own two feet.

'What is it?' he asked, his hands still on her shoulders.

She ran a hand distractedly through her hair. 'Tony,' she said with a nervous little laugh, 'I'm not sure I'm ready for this.'

He dropped his hands from her shoulders. 'I don't understand.'

She glanced up at him. The puzzled expression had become a frown, his brow furrowed, his eyes narrowed. A little thrill of fear ran through her. He was so big! So strong! What if he were to turn ugly?

She dropped her eyes from his. 'You're just moving a little too fast for me, that's all,' she said with a shrug.

'I see.' His voice was tight with pent-up emotion. 'So are you telling me it was all an act? That you didn't want me as much as I wanted you? Sorry, Stacey, I don't believe that. Unless ...'

She gave him a quick look. 'Unless what?' she asked in a small voice.

The corners of his mouth quirked upward in a sardonic smile. 'Unless you've just been stringing me along, playing the tease.'

'No!' she cried, horrified. 'I would never do that. I just—just——' She cleared her throat and looked directly into his eyes.

At the sight of that sneering expression, something seemed to snap inside her. Who was he to call all the shots here? Why weren't her wishes in the matter just as valid as his? She straightened up, stiffening her back and squaring her shoulders.

'I just don't think that a few kisses necessarily lead directly to bed, that's all,' she announced firmly.

Their eyes locked in mortal combat for a few long seconds. Then he made a small noise of disgust deep in his throat and waved a hand in the air.

'A man can take just so much of this, you know,' he said in a low voice. 'I've played it your way for weeks now, let you call all the shots. Now it's rapidly becoming quite clear that we're not going anywhere with this thing.'

She folded her arms across her chest and gave him a challenging look. 'Well, just where is it you want to go, Tony?' she demanded. 'You've made it quite clear right from the beginning that you don't want a commitment of any kind. And I don't want a meaningless affair. What else is there?'

His face darkened and he opened his mouth, then snapped it shut. 'Nothing, obviously,' he said in a clipped voice. Then he nodded briskly. 'And, in that case, I guess there's nothing left for me to do but say goodnight and go home.'

He turned on his heel then, and strode away from her. Aghast, she stared after him. Was that it? No discussion? Nothing more to be said? Was he just going to walk out of her life as abruptly as he'd burst into it?

She stood there, rooted to the spot, heard the front door open and close, then silence. Everything in her wanted to run after him, beg him to come back, agree to whatever he wanted from her. But she didn't. She couldn't.

It wasn't until much later, as she was lying in bed, tossing and turning, trying to make sense out of what had happened, that she was finally able to face the truth. She had never been in control of the situation. That was all an illusion.

He'd held all the cards right from the beginning, playing with her like a cat with a mouse. It was all a game to him. First he'd held out a little bait—that night of the gold chain episode, the insinuating innuendoes. Then he'd backed off at the first sign of resistance from her, certain she'd wonder why, whetting her appetite for more.

And of course it had worked. Almost. He'd been very angry tonight—frustrated, too—and in a way she couldn't really blame him. Why should a man like Tony waste his time on her when there must be a long line of women who'd jump at the chance to have an affair with him?

She was well out of it, and should be grateful all she'd suffered was a bruised ego. If she'd followed her own inclinations, given in to her own wayward desire for him, it could have been devastating.

CHAPTER FIVE

THE next day was Sunday, and although Stacey was still shaken by the emotionally-charged scene with Tony, she did have a life of her own, and goals to pursue that didn't include him. Her classes would resume next week, and she spent the day organizing her clothes and cleaning the apartment so that she'd be able to meet her busy schedule without worrying about the trivia of daily life.

There was no sign of Tony for the next few days. Not a sound came from the apartment across the hall, nor did she come across him in the lobby or the elevator. He was either out of town again on business or deliberately avoiding her, which was more likely after their last tense encounter, and she had to wonder, with something like awe, at the uncanny ability men seemed to have for always managing to put a woman in the wrong, no matter how bad their own behavior.

She tried to be philosophical. It was a dead-end situation. She couldn't possibly come out of it unscathed. All her illusions about controlling the course of the affair were pure fantasy. She was better off without him. She had plans of her own that didn't include him anyway.

Thus she would recite the litany of all the good reasons why it was just as well he had dropped out of her life, that she was free of the man's disturbing presence in it. Still, she continued to hesitate whenever she passed his door, to look for him in the lobby, and, alone in her chaste bed at night, she couldn't quite fight down the image of flashing blue eyes, quick smile and tall, masculine form that haunted even her dreams.

New Yorkers had been enjoying a spell of unseasonably mild weather lately, an early harbinger of spring, with sunny skies and fairly balmy temperatures for early March.

On Wednesday morning, however, when Stacey glanced out her window before leaving for work, she noticed that it had clouded over and was sprinkling lightly. Better wear her light raincoat and take a scarf, she decided. Outside, as she hurried toward her bus stop, she noticed that there was a heavy bank of black clouds to the north and a distinct chill in the air, but by now it was too late to go back for warmer clothes. Her bus was already pulling up to the curb.

Richard had obviously worked over the weekend, and she was especially busy all morning, transcribing the tapes he'd left her, even eating her lunch at her desk to catch up. Then that afternoon he called her into his office to help him set up a file for his new breakfast cereal account.

She noticed that he seemed rather abstracted, as though he had something on his mind, but she had realized by now that busy advertising account executives were always worried about something, so didn't mention it to him.

He had finished his last instruction, and she was just getting up from her chair, when he cleared his throat and motioned her to sit back down.

'I haven't seen much of you lately,' he began. 'Outside of the office, I mean.'

'Well, you've been busy. And you know what my schedule is like.'

'I've tried to call you a few times—last Saturday night, in fact. But you didn't answer.'

'Well, no,' she replied, flushing a little. 'I wasn't home.'

There was a pause as he gazed at her expectantly, obviously waiting for her to explain. 'Anything interesting?' he asked lightly at last.

She gave a nervous laugh. 'Well, as a matter of fact, I went to the opera for the first time. *Carmen.*'

He raised a sandy eyebrow. 'Oh? Did you enjoy it?'

'Yes. Very much.' She knew quite well he was hoping she would elaborate, but Richard didn't own her, she told herself stoutly. She didn't have to answer to him for her actions.

'Well,' he said, after a few moments, 'perhaps that explains why you've been looking particularly well lately. In fact,' he commented, in a rather strained voice, 'I've noticed a kind of glow about you for some time now.'

'Why, thank you, Richard,' she replied. 'I'm glad you think so.' Then she had to smile. 'But I must say you don't sound very happy about it.'

'Sorry. I guess I was just wondering if that new sparkle in your eyes could be caused by a man. Then, when you mentioned the opera, well . . .' He shrugged diffidently. 'It doesn't take a mental giant to put two and two together.'

She opened her mouth to protest, but then snapped it shut again. She didn't want to lie to him, but neither did she want to tell him she'd been seeing Tony. Since it was all over between them anyway, even before it had really begun, there really wasn't any point in troubling Richard about it.

'It couldn't be that good-looking new neighbor of yours, by any chance?' he asked lightly. 'You know, the guy who came to use your telephone and stood there ogling you in that green dress.'

As her mind flashed back to that evening she remembered it had also been the night Richard thought he recognized Tony's name. Even though she knew she'd probably never see him again, it still nagged at her how he was so vague, almost secretive, about his work, and how he always managed to slide out of any discussion of it.

Nor could she quite forget the ugly little scene with poor Mr Pomeroy the night of the opera, the desperation in his face. Tony had been like a rock, a block of solid ice, blind and deaf to the man's problem.

Now Richard had given her the opening she needed, and she seized it quickly. 'Actually, I've been meaning to ask you about him myself.'

'Really? What could I possibly tell you?'

'Well, if you recall, you thought you recognized him, or at least his name.'

He frowned thoughtfully. 'Did I? Gosh, Stacey, I've been so swamped with this new account it's completely slipped my mind. Tony something, wasn't it?'

'Devereux. Tony Devereux. Anthony, actually.'

'Ah, yes. Didn't we decide he couldn't be the man I had in mind, not living in that rent-controlled apartment?'

'Yes, but I thought you might have had second thoughts by now.'

He laughed. 'To tell you the truth, I haven't had any thoughts at all on the matter.' He eyed her narrowly. 'Why the sudden interest? Has he been making a nuisance of himself? Or could he be the reason for the new sparkle in your eyes?'

She reddened. 'Oh, it's just that living right across the hall from him we're bound to run into each other, and I'm naturally curious about him. He seems to work odd hours and travels a great deal.'

'I'll look into it for you, if you like.'

'Oh, no,' she said hastily, rising to her feet again. 'No need to do that. It's not important.'

When she left work late that afternoon and stepped out on to the busy street, thronging with homebound commuters, she was appalled to see that the early morning drizzle had turned into a light snowfall. Unusual for early March, but not unheard of.

She'd come away that morning with no boots, no gloves and no umbrella, only her lightweight raincoat and a thin scarf. Tying it hastily around her head and buttoning her coat up tight, she dashed down the pavement through the swirling white flakes to her bus stop.

The bus was late, of course, and as she stood on the corner waiting for it, freezing, she could feel the snow soaking through her scarf and drifting into her shoes, so that when it finally arrived, her head and feet were both damp.

By the time she got off at her stop the gentle drifts had turned into a steady deluge, the air thick with the heavy white stuff. A brisk wind had come up off Long Island Sound, and it looked to be fast becoming a full-scale blizzard. She still had two long blocks to go after the bus let her off, and by the time she arrived at her building, she was numb with cold.

Her apartment was freezing, since she'd turned the heat off as usual that morning. What she wanted was a good hot bath, but first she turned on the furnace. While the place warmed up she took off her wet clothes and put on a warm robe, then went into the kitchen to make herself a cup of hot, strong tea.

When it was done and she had just carried it to the living-room and gone to the window, sipping the scalding liquid and gazing out at the heavy drifts of swirling snow, the doorbell rang.

Tony! she thought immediately—and, she realized in the next moment, totally unreasonably. Of course it wouldn't be him. There was no reason for her to expect him to show up at this point.

Still, with a distinct lift to her heart, she set her cup down and ran to answer it.

Of course it wasn't Tony at all. Instead a young man in jeans and sweatshirt with a bored expression on his face stood there, waiting while she opened the door, obviously a delivery boy, since he was carrying a long package.

'Stacey Sinclair?' he asked in a strong Brooklyn accent.

'Yes.'

He thrust the box at her. 'Package for you.'

'For me?' she asked, somewhat taken aback. 'Are you sure?'

The boy grinned. 'Yeah, if you're who you say you are, I am.'

'Well, thank you,' she murmured, taking the box from him and returning his smile. 'I'm surprised you're making deliveries at all in this weather.'

'Oh, we're like the postal service,' he explained airily. 'We can get through anything.'

She hesitated for a moment, wondering if she should give him a tip. However, since he had already turned on his heel and was now sauntering down the hall to the elevator, whistling loudly, she decided he must not expect one.

Back inside her apartment she set the box down, loosened the string that was tied around it, and lifted the lid. There, nestled on a layer of green tissue paper, were at least three dozen gorgeous yellow roses, each bud perfect. She smiled down at the lovely sight. On one or two occasions in the past Richard had sent her flowers, but this time he'd really outdone himself.

Then she saw that there was a small envelope lying on top. When she tore it open and pulled out the card, she immediately recognized the same slashing black handwriting she'd seen once before on Hannah's mailbox.

'To Stacey with love,' she read. 'Yours, Tony.'

That was all. But it was enough. The two key words—'love' and 'yours'—were all she needed. Grinning foolishly, she ran into the kitchen to put the roses in water, then set the vase on the coffee table in the living-room.

Still clutching the card, she sat down on the couch and re-read it, even though she already knew the short message by heart. She must mean something to him, something important, for a man like Tony to have committed himself even that far.

Now the question was, what should she do? Still debating, she went into the bathroom to run her tub. While she was soaking the answer suddenly came to her. If he had indeed been out of town the past few days, he must be back. Why not just do what she *wanted* to do? Run across the hall and throw herself into his arms.

Hopping out of the cooling tub, she dried off swiftly, then pulled on a pair of jeans and a heavy pullover and ran to the door, her heart racing madly in anticipation, her spirits soaring with renewed hope.

She slid the bolt, pulled the door open, and was just about to step out into the hall when she noticed that someone was standing in front of Tony's apartment. A woman, as a matter of fact, a rather tall brunette.

Her back was toward Stacey, but even so there was something about her casual, confident stance, the sleek mink coat she was wearing, the very high-heeled shoes, the long, flowing dark hair spreading over her shoulders, that told Stacey that here was a very sophisticated, probably very beautiful, and at the least very self-assured woman.

She stood there for a moment, staring blankly, then began to back cautiously into her own apartment, hoping the woman hadn't noticed her. She was just about to shut her door quietly when she saw Tony's own door open. She couldn't see him from where she

was standing, but she did still have a good view of
his visitor and could hear her greeting to him quite
clearly.

'Tony, darling!' she cried, holding her arms wide,
as though anticipating a warm embrace. 'You see I
made it through the storm after all.'

She then stepped inside, most likely into Tony's
waiting arms, and the door was shut behind her.
Stacey slunk back, closed her own door quietly, locked
it securely and leaned back against it, her eyes closed,
her heart pounding, all her renewed hopes shattered.

By the next morning, of course, after wrestling all
through the night with jealous suspicions, she had
come to her senses. The woman could be anybody. A
relative, perhaps. Of course he'd said he didn't have
any family, but he might well have left out a distant
cousin. Or someone from his office.

He *had* sent her the beautiful roses, after all. That
morning they were still right there in plain sight, on
the coffee table in the living-room where she'd set them
the night before. That had to mean something.

In any case, there was no need to panic just because
he'd had an evening visitor. She should have learned
by now not to judge a situation by appearances. It
was only sheer chance that she'd seen the woman
arrive.

Feeling much better, even rather proud of her
mature attitude, she got ready for work as usual,
and set off for the office. She did linger for a
moment right outside Tony's door, listening for any
sign of him, but it was silent as the grave, and she
hurried on.

She had just stepped inside the elevator, and the doors were about to close, when she heard someone call out down the hall and the sound of footsteps running toward her.

'Would you hold that car please?' came a woman's voice.

Stacey reached out to catch the door before it closed, and held it open, waiting. In a moment the woman arrived, a little breathless, and all Stacey could do was stare blankly at her. It was the same woman she'd seen outside Tony's door last night!

She flashed Stacey a brilliant smile. 'Thanks very much,' she said, stepping inside.

'You're welcome,' Stacey replied stiffly. 'Lobby?'

The woman nodded. 'Yes, please.'

Stacey punched the button and the car, always sluggish in the morning, began to lurch slowly downward.

By now she had collected herself enough to give the brunette a more careful scrutiny. She was indeed everything she'd imagined last night when all she'd seen was the back of her: quite beautiful, with fine, rather aristocratic features, a head of long shiny raven-black hair, and swathed in the same mink coat.

She also looked a little tousled this morning. Of course, Stacey thought bitterly. What could you expect when she'd obviously spent the night with Tony? Even so, her appearance was so striking that she made Stacey feel like a dowdy frump.

Although she was seething inwardly, however, her curiosity had begun to outweigh her anger. 'I haven't seen you around,' she said in a pleasant voice. 'Have you just moved in recently?'

'Oh, no,' the woman replied, with a silvery little laugh. 'Just visiting a friend.' She gave Stacey a knowing, woman-to-woman smile, making it crystal-clear just how good a friend she'd been visiting.

As more people crowded in the elevator the two women became separated. Then, by the time they reached the lobby and all the passengers began to pour out, the striking brunette was already gone.

It was just as well, Stacey thought as she trudged glumly toward her bus stop. There really wasn't anything they had to say to each other.

Somehow she got through that day. Luckily Richard was away at meetings until five o'clock, so she didn't have to face him, and he'd left her so much work to do that she was able to distract her mind temporarily from the rage that simmered within her. She was grateful too that the semester break was nearly over. At least now she'd have schoolwork to occupy her mind instead of these dismal thoughts about Tony and his overnight visitor.

She should have known better. It had been plain right from the beginning that he was way out of her league—in experience, in confidence, and in expertise in the game of love. He'd only been manipulating her the whole time, and her only question now was why he'd bothered in the first place, when he had women like last night's brunette obviously at his beck and call.

Probably just the thrill of the chase, she decided gloomily on her way home that evening. To a man like Tony Devereux, any resistance would constitute a challenge he couldn't resist. The flowers had merely been a bone tossed to her, and all that talk about his own frustrations had been so much hot air!

At some point she'd have to deal with him. Surely sending her the roses, with that particular message, meant he'd seek her out eventually, and she needed to think how best to handle the inevitable confrontation. On the one hand she was dying to see his face when she told him about her discovery of his brunette playmate, but on the other she'd be happier never to see him again at all.

At least the weather had improved. Last night's storm had passed, bringing another warming trend, along with a light drizzle. The accumulation of snow had started melting that morning, and by the time she got off the bus it was almost gone.

As it turned out, she was saved having to make any decision when Tony himself emerged from his apartment just as she was unlocking her door.

She stiffened and stood there as though paralyzed, her key still in the lock. Her heart started to pound erratically, her knees felt weak, and there was a ringing sensation in her ears.

'Ah, there you are,' he said, coming up behind her. 'Right on time. I thought I'd take you out for a special dinner tonight, someplace quiet where we can talk.'

Suddenly an icy calm descended on her. Somehow just the sound of his voice, that same old maddening confident tone, not to mention his bland assumption that even after entertaining another woman in his apartment all night he could so blithely move on to his plans for her, settled her nerves completely.

She turned slowly around. He was dressed in a dark business suit, as though he'd just come from his office, and a few drops of rain still sparkled in his dark hair under the light in the hall. In fact, he looked wonderful, and she steeled herself against him.

'Talk about what, Tony?' she asked.

The smile on his face faded. 'About us, of course,' he said at last in a low voice.

'Sorry,' she said briskly. 'I haven't the time tonight.'

With that, she sailed inside and started to close the door in his face. However, something seemed to be obstructing it, and she looked down to see a rather large, very polished cordovan loafer blocking the way.

'Would you kindly remove your foot from my doorway?' she requested in a lofty tone.

'What the devil . . . ?' he growled. 'No!' he barked. 'I sure as hell won't. Not until you tell me what's going on.'

Before she realized his intention, he'd pushed past her and was inside her living-room, the door shut behind him. They stood there for several long seconds, glaring at each other, Stacey with her arms folded in front of her, Tony with his hands clenched into fists and held rigidly at his sides.

He turned from her then and walked over to the couch, and stood there for a moment gazing down at the vase of yellow roses set on the table before it, his long legs spread apart, his hands in his pockets, as though marshaling his thoughts.

When she came up slowly to stand beside him, he turned to her. For a moment he didn't speak, but in the end a faint smile did begin to twitch at the corners of his mouth.

'Well,' he said finally, 'I see you got the flowers. Rather pretty, aren't they?'

'Yes, they are,' she said stiffly. 'They arrived last night. In fact I was just on my way to your place to thank you for them, but then——' She broke off with a shrug as she heard her voice falter and felt the tears sting behind her eyes.

He took a step toward her, one hand held out. 'Stacey,' he said softly. 'What is it? What's wrong?'

She shrank back immediately. 'Don't come any closer, Tony. I warn you. None of your tricks. They won't work any more with me.'

He raked his fingers through his hair and gave her a look of utter bafflement. 'What are you going to do? Make me guess? Play twenty questions with you?' His face hardened. 'Just tell me what's wrong and let's get it over with.'

She'd had enough by now. 'All right!' she cried. 'I will. I'm afraid it's just not your lucky day, Tony. By sheer chance I just happened to see your visitor arrive last night.'

'Oh, that,' he said, with a dismissive wave of his hand. 'That was only Andrea. She's ancient history. In fact she's married now, living in Connecticut. She just happened to be in the city yesterday and decided to drop in to say hello.'

'My goodness,' Stacey said, smiling grimly and giving him a look of mock understanding. 'That explains everything, doesn't it? How could I possibly have misunderstood?' Then her face froze in an expression of utter contempt. 'Especially when I rode down on the elevator with her this morning.'

For a moment he actually looked abashed, and a deep red flush washed over his face. But only for a split-second, and in the next moment he had recovered completely.

'If you'll recall,' he drawled maddeningly, 'we got hit with a freak blizzard last night. She couldn't leave. Traffic was snarled from here to Long Island. She called for a taxi and they just laughed at her. Even the trains weren't running. What was I supposed to do? Turn her out in the snow?' He shook his head. 'I'm afraid you've jumped to the wrong conclusion here, Stacey.'

'And I'm afraid you've lost every bit of credibility you ever had with me, Tony.'

'Now, listen,' he said in a warning tone, obviously growing hot under the collar himself by now. 'I've done all the explaining I'm going to. I've told you the simple truth. You can either believe me or not. It's up to you.'

'Well, that's easy,' she retorted instantly. 'I don't. You've played cat and mouse with me from day one, Tony, and I'm sick of it. Maybe you are telling the truth about last night. I don't know. I don't even care much any more. I just know the kind of games you play are too sophisticated, too complicated for me. I don't need that kind of aggravation.'

He stared at her in stark disbelief, as though she'd suddenly announced she'd decided to take a short trip to Mars the next day. He ran his fingers through his hair again, then began to pace around the room. Stacey stood there watching him, filled with an intense sense of satisfaction that she'd finally made a dent in that bland, maddening composure of his.

And, even as she watched, she knew quite well that she was going to regret the stand she was taking, but at the same time a little voice deep inside her told her she was doing the right thing, even if he was telling the truth. A sudden vision of Mr Pomeroy rose up in her mind, and memories of Tony's secretiveness about his work. *Something* definitely was wrong. It might not be his brunette, his Andrea, but there had to be something else he was hiding, something important, and she was sick and tired of trying to deal with his deception.

He had come to stand before her now, and stood there gazing down at her, his brow like thunder, his face livid one moment, pinched and white the next, his features working as though he couldn't quite find the right words.

'Would you care to tell me,' he snarled, 'just what my purpose in all that intrigue you accuse me of might be?'

'That's quite obvious!' she snapped back.

'Oh? And would you please enlighten me as to my motives?'

She gave a dry, humorless laugh. 'You've had one thing on your mind all along. Why don't you just admit it?'

'And what might that be?'

'You know quite well. I don't have to explain anything to you.'

He rubbed a hand over the back of his neck and shook his head slowly from side to side. 'I know what *you* think it is,' he said in a weary voice. 'You seem to have some idea that all I ever wanted was to hustle you into bed, and that's simply not true. What do you take me for? Do I really appear that desperate to you? Hasn't it ever occurred to you that I like being

with you?' His bright blue eyes flashed at her.
'Although God knows why.'

More shaken than she cared to admit by his obviously sincere statements, she still wasn't ready to
capitulate. 'And bed has nothing to do with it!' she
finally replied.

'Well, for God's sake, Stacey, even if it does, don't
you find that even mildly flattering?' He stood there
glaring down at her, then finally made a noise of
disgust deep in his throat and put his hands on his
hips. 'You're crazy!' he barked out. 'Paranoid! Stark
raving mad!' He thrust his face down close to hers.
'Do you want to know what I think?'

She opened her mouth to tell him that she em-
phatically did not, but before she could get a word
out, he'd started in again.

'I think the problem with you—with us, for that
matter—is your own insecurities. All this fooling
around we've been doing, for weeks now, ever since
we first met! First you run hot, then you run cold.
One minute you've got me convinced you're eager for
love, the next you're an iceberg.'

'Love!' she spat out. 'What do you know about
love? All you want is a meaningless affair. Probably
several at one time.'

'And what is it *you* want, Stacey?' he asked in an
icy tone. 'You've managed to keep it a secret from
me so far,' he went on, with a dramatic wave of one
arm. 'Would you care to enlighten me now?'

She pulled herself up to her full five feet seven
inches, thrust out her chin, and stared straight into
his blazing blue eyes. 'All right! I'll tell you,' she an-

nounced, pointing imperiously at the door. 'I want you to get out of my apartment and never come back.'

'Gladly!' he bit out.

With his accusations still ringing in her ears, and the sinking feeling that he might be right, but so fueled by hurt and anger by now that she was beyond caring, she watched him as he whirled around and stalked away from her toward the door. But then, to her astonishment, before going through it and slamming it hard behind him, he stopped cold, one hand on the knob.

He stood there for several moments, his back to her, his head bent, as though deep in thought. For a wild moment Stacey wondered if he was debating whether to come back and do her bodily harm, but when he finally did turn back to her he was actually smiling, albeit grudgingly, and the expression on his face looked suspiciously like self-satisfaction to her.

'I think I know what's really eating you,' he remarked in an offhand tone as he walked slowly toward her.

She tossed her head. 'And what might that be?' she demanded loftily.

'You're jealous.'

'Don't be ridiculous!' she retorted.

But in the next instant she had to admit he was probably right. What she'd felt when she saw that woman standing there last night, saw that she'd still been there that morning, was an insane unreasonable jealousy.

She'd been behaving like a silly schoolgirl. He'd given her a perfectly plausible explanation for his nocturnal visitor. He'd sent her the lovely roses *before* the woman showed up. And in her heart she believed he was telling her the truth about that. What reason was there for him to lie? He was a free agent, after all. He hadn't made any commitments or promises, in fact had gone out of his way to avoid them.

Suddenly all the anger drained out of her. She looked up at him, and when she saw that he was grinning at her, his own anger clearly dissipated, she couldn't help returning the smile.

'All right,' she said grudgingly. 'I guess you've got a point.'

He heaved a deep sigh. 'Now,' he said. 'We need to talk. Can we please sit down?'

'All right.'

She picked up the newspaper still spread out on the couch from that morning, laid it on the table by the roses, and sat down, waiting for him, her hands folded in her lap, every muscle tense.

CHAPTER SIX

TONY sat down heavily beside her, then leaned forward, his elbows resting on his knees, hands clasped in front of him, staring fixedly down at the carpet.

Finally he turned to her. 'I've been away for a few days on business, and while I was gone——' He broke off, then shrugged diffidently and gave her a crooked smile. 'Well, I missed you.'

Warmth flooded through her at the unexpected admission, not least because he seemed so grudging about making it.

She smiled at him. 'You don't sound very happy about it.'

He sighed again, and leaned back on the couch, eyeing her balefully. 'Well, to tell you the truth, I'm not.' He shook his head. 'I don't know what it is about you, Stacey. You're a very maddening woman, and by rights I should shake you within an inch of your life.' He lifted his broad shoulders. 'Instead, I have to admit that I don't want to give up our...' He paused for a moment, searching for a word. 'Our friendship, I guess you'd call it for lack of a more precise word.'

'But that night we went to the opera you said...'

'I know what I said!' he barked angrily. 'Do you think it's any picnic for me to admit I might have been wrong? Can't a man change his mind?'

'Well, yes, I guess so, but nothing has really changed, has it? I mean, in a way you were right.

You've made it perfectly clear you're not interested in any kind of commitment, and I can't get involved in a meaningless affair, so...'

'What makes you think it would be meaningless?' he asked in a low voice. He reached out to take her hand in his. 'Surely you know by now that I do care about you. A lot. More than I would have thought possible, for such a stubborn woman. I'm willing to play by your rules, whatever they might be, at least for a time. What more can I do or say to prove it to you?'

You could tell me you loved me, she agonized silently. You could make room for me in your life, your plans for the future. But she couldn't say any of that to him.

She looked over at him, mute with a sudden longing. The feel of his large warm hand holding hers was fast melting all her powers of resistance. He meant what he said, she had no doubt, but how long could she hope to hold a man like Tony Devereux with chaste goodnight kisses and hand-holding?

All her illusions about being in control were just that—mere illusions. In the end he'd most likely get exactly what he wanted from her, and not least of all, she added ruefully, because deep down, if she'd only admit it, it was actually what she herself wanted.

'Listen,' he went on, breaking into her thoughts and moving a little closer to her, 'if you're worried about my extra-curricular activities, that's one thing you can count on. Whatever we have together, wherever it's going, as far as I'm concerned it's an exclusive arrangement.'

She gave him a swift glance. By every standard of common sense she should send him packing. What kind of 'arrangement' was he offering her? Only that he wouldn't sleep around while they were involved with each other. The trouble was, he was so close to her now that she could feel his hard shoulder pressing against hers, smell the faint scent of soap and the aftershave he used, and her mind simply wasn't able to function sensibly.

His arm snaked around her shoulders and he drew her up against him more closely. 'Come on, Stacey,' he murmured in her ear. 'Be a sport. I'm putty in your hands. What do you have to lose?'

Still troubled, she turned her head slightly toward him to get a closer look at his face, hoping to read something there to reassure her. It was a mistake, however, because the moment she did so, his dark head bent down, and the next thing she knew his mouth was pressed against hers in a long, exquisitely tender kiss.

She was lost and she knew it. All she could do was nestle against him, close her eyes, and enjoy the intense thrill, the deep satisfaction, of being in this man's arms again. The future would just have to take care of itself.

After a long moment he drew his head back and grinned down at her, smoothing the wayward wisps of hair back from her forehead. 'Let's say we're going steady,' he said with a mocking smile. 'Pretend we're teenagers again.'

'Now you're making fun of me,' she protested feebly.

He sobered instantly. 'No. Don't ever think that. I admit you keep me in a constant state of frustration, but I find there's something very refreshing about your brand of chastity.' He gave her a wicked grin. 'Perhaps it's the challenge that appeals to me.'

'Tony!' she cried, drawing back. 'It's not a game!'

'I know, I know,' he said, his arms tightening around her. 'Can't you be as gracious in victory as I am in defeat?'

Still not quite reassured, she dropped her head back on his shoulder. Somehow she couldn't see him admitting to defeat, much less giving in to her wishes, and she had the sinking feeling that although she might have won this battle, the war was far from over.

True to his word, from that night on Tony seemed to be making every effort to practice restraint in his lovemaking, and while Stacey appreciated this, she soon came to realize it wasn't going to work.

Not only was he becoming visibly more withdrawn, she herself was more and more frustrated by his almost chaste goodnight kisses, the way he hardly touched her any more, even in the most casual or impersonal way.

Finally, she'd had enough. On a Thursday night, a few weeks later, they had just come home from dinner and a movie. As had become his custom, after she'd unlocked her door, he gave her his usual brief kiss, said goodnight, and turned to go.

'Tony,' she said, putting a hand on his arm.

'Yes?'

'Come inside for a minute, will you?'

He frowned. 'I don't know if that's such a good idea.'

'Well, actually, that's what I want to talk to you about.'

'All right.'

Inside, he sat down on the living-room couch, waiting for her while she took off her coat. After she'd hung it up, she came to sit beside him, trying to think how to broach the subject she had on her mind.

Finally, she turned to him. 'Tony, I don't think we should see each other any more.'

His eyes flew open and his face darkened. 'Well, that's a shocker,' he said at last, leaning back on the couch and eyeing her suspiciously. 'Why on earth not?'

She shrugged helplessly. 'Well, isn't it obvious?' She gave him a wan smile. 'Surely you're not happy with this—this—arrangement.'

'Have I complained?'

'Well, no,' she said slowly. 'But I do have the distinct impression that you're sort of...' She hesitated again, groping for the right word. 'I don't know. Withdrawing from me.'

'Well, my God, Stacey!' he ground out angrily. 'What the hell do you want from me?' He reached over and took her hand. 'I've played strictly by your rules for the past few weeks,' he went on in a softer tone. 'No pushing. Hands off.' He grinned. 'Lots of cold showers. Just tell me what it is you want. I can't read your mind, you know.'

'That's just the trouble,' she replied miserably. 'I don't know what I want. But it all seems rather pointless, doesn't it? I mean, we only seem to be floundering aimlessly.'

'Well I know what *I* want,' he stated firmly. 'I've never made any secret of it. And I think if you were more honest with yourself you'd admit it's what you want, too.'

Taken a little off-base by his bald statement, she gave him a direct look. As their eyes locked together she felt she was drowning in those sapphire-blue pools. She also suspected that he might be right, and when in the next moment he shifted closer to her and his hand slid slowly up her bare arm, the sudden explosive shock she felt at his touch proved it to her beyond a doubt.

'Oh, Tony!' she said with feeling. 'I don't know what to do.'

He put an arm around her and drew her head down on his shoulder. As he continued to stroke her arm for the first time in weeks she felt she was where she was meant to be, close beside the man she loved. Yes, she had to admit it. She was helplessly, hopelessly in love with him and wanted him, all of him, on any terms.

When she felt his lips press against her cheek, she turned her head instinctively toward him. For a brief moment their eyes met again, then, with a groaning sound deep in his throat, he dipped his head lower and covered her mouth with his in a deep, satisfying kiss.

After a long moment he drew back. 'I think,' he said in a low, deliberate tone, 'that I might have a solution. At least a suggestion.'

Breathless by now from the sheer joy of being in his arms again, she only nodded.

'My company has a lakeside cabin in Vermont,' he went on. 'Very remote, very private. How about going up there with me for a few days?'

She stiffened immediately. 'Oh, Tony, I don't know.'

'Now, hold on a minute. Don't just reject the idea out of hand. Nothing needs to happen that you don't want to happen.' He cupped her chin in his hand, forcing her to meet his gaze. 'Do you trust me, Stacey?' he asked softly.

She nodded. 'Yes. I do.'

'Then you know I won't push you into anything you're not ready for. I think I've already proved that. I just think we need to get away—from jobs, from school, from this damned apartment situation—be by ourselves for a while, get to know each other better. How about it?'

She drew away from him and sat staring down at her hands, biting her lip, trying to decide. Everything in her wanted to agree. Almost everything, that was. It seemed only her cautious nature was holding her back. It sounded like heaven—two or three days alone with this man, nothing and no one to interfere.

Finally, she smiled at him. 'Well, I'll admit it's a tempting offer,' she said. 'But I need a few days to think about it.'

A fleeting frown passed over his face, but then he smiled. 'All right. Fair enough. The ball is in your court.' He jumped to his feet. 'Now, I think I'd better leave.' He made a face and added ruefully, 'It's cold shower time again.'

*   *   *

She lay awake half the night, debating the pros and cons of Tony's proposition, and by the next morning she was no closer to a decision.

Of course she wanted to go with him, more than anything. Then what was holding her back? Simple prudery? In this day and age? She didn't think so. If only he'd said one word of love, she would have agreed immediately. Was he simply trying to manipulate her again? Or was he on the cutting edge of a serious commitment?

The cool sunny weather was over by the end of the week. A heavy bank of clouds began to move down from Canada and, on the Tuesday of the following week, the imminent storm finally burst. Stacey had to splash her way to the bus after work that night, through all the puddles that had collected on the pavement from the heavy rains, with thunder and lightning crashing overhead.

When the bus finally came, all the seats were taken, since the storm had brought out far more riders than usual, and she stood there, her feet squishing in her wet shoes, her thin headscarf soaked through, shivering even in the overheated bus.

By the time she finally got off at her stop, the worst of the storm seemed to have passed, the booming of the thunder no longer directly overhead, but it was still pouring, and Stacey ran the two short blocks to her building getting wetter by the second, until finally she pushed the door open and stepped gratefully inside the heated lobby.

Untying her scarf and shaking it out as she went, she had just started slogging her way toward the elevator when she caught sight of Peggy Connors, who had obviously just come in herself and looked as wet and miserable as Stacey felt.

'Hi, stranger,' Peggy called to her. 'I see you got caught in the storm, too.'

'Yes, isn't it awful? I'm drenched.'

They started walking toward the elevator together. 'Well, I haven't seen you for a while,' Peggy commented in a somewhat accusing tone as she punched the 'up' button.

Stacey flushed guiltily. She'd missed the last two meetings of the condominium committee. Somehow, with her almost total absorption in the Tony Devereux situation, she'd rather lost interest in the whole subject. Now, with Peggy's reminder, she had to wonder how on earth she could have forgotten the fact that she'd lose her home soon if something wasn't done about it.

'Well, yes,' she mumbled. 'I've been awfully busy.'

'So I've gathered,' Peggy replied with a knowing smile. 'I've seen you a few times with your current "business".' She gave Stacey an accusing look. 'You were supposed to put in a word for me with that dishy hunk, if you'll recall.'

The flush on Stacey's face deepened into a brick-red. 'How in the world...?' she began.

'Only kidding,' Peggy replied with a laugh. The elevator arrived just then and they stepped inside. 'And green with envy. To answer your question, I've seen you together a few times. Lucky you! Is he as nice as he is great-looking?'

Stacey could only mumble an incoherent reply, but Peggy wasn't really listening to her anyway. 'As for the committee, if you're still interested, I could bring you up to date on our progress. What there is of it, that is,' she added gloomily. 'How about stopping by my place for a drink now? You look as though you could use something to warm you up a little.'

'Sure, Peggy,' she replied swiftly. What she really wanted to do was get out of her wet clothes and into a hot bath, but she was so anxious to get back in her friend's good graces that she had to agree. 'I'd like that. And I am definitely still interested. I need this place as badly as you do.'

In Peggy's apartment they discussed the committee's plans, which hadn't changed as far as Stacey could see; they were still counting on delaying tactics as their only weapon against the conversion.

'Actually,' Peggy went on glumly, 'the only real piece of helpful information we've come up with is the name of the corporation that's behind the apartment management—Global Enterprises.'

Stacey sipped her wine, listening with only half an ear as Peggy rambled on, her mind still on the subject of the trip with Tony. Should she or shouldn't she?

Suddenly Stacey was startled by a sharp jab in the arm. She jumped and turned to Peggy, to see an expression of the deepest disgust on her face.

'You haven't heard a word I've said,' Peggy protested indignantly. 'Your mind seems to be a million miles away. On lover-boy, I suppose.' She reached over to refill their wine-glasses. 'Is there a problem?'

Suddenly Stacey felt the need to confide in her friend, to hear another woman's point of view. She and Peggy hadn't been close, both of them were too busy for that, but she'd always found her warm and friendly—a little flippant, but someone she thought she could count on in a pinch.

'Well, to tell you the truth, I am concerned about something. Not a problem, exactly. I mean, we get along fine. It's just that he wants me to go away with him for a few days, and I can't seem to make up my mind whether I should.'

Peggy stared at her, eyes wide with utter disbelief. 'You've got to be kidding!' she finally exploded. 'You have the outrageous good fortune to catch the most attractive man in this building, possibly in the whole city of New York, and you wonder whether to go away with him when he asks you?' She shook her head. 'I don't believe it! I can't see why you're even hesitating.'

'Then I take it you think I should go,' Stacey said, smiling.

'Go! I can't think of one good reason why you shouldn't, and about a hundred why you should. This is the nineteen-nineties, Stacey, not the eighteen-hundreds. You've been married. What reason could you possibly have for not going? Unless you don't care enough about him, and in that case please pass him along to me.'

'Oh, I care,' Stacey said. 'It's not that. I guess I'm just not quite sure he does.'

'But, my dear girl, how could you possibly imagine he doesn't care? He asked you to go, didn't he?'

'Well, yes.'

'Then that proves it. Of course he cares. What do you want, for heaven's sake? A written guarantee? An oath of undying love?' She eyed Stacey carefully. 'Ah, I get it. It's the "C" word that has you ham-strung, isn't it?'

Stacey gave her a puzzled look. 'The "C" word?'

'Sure, you know. Commitment. You're afraid to enjoy this gorgeous man, who you admit you care about, because he hasn't committed himself. Or won't. Well, forget it. Take what you can get when you can get it, that's my motto. You may get your heart broken a few times along the way, but,' she added with a grin, 'you'll end up with some great memories.'

Then a light dawned in the light gray eyes and she gave Stacey a knowing look. 'Unless it's Richard you're worried about.'

'Well, yes. At least partly,' Stacey admitted. 'I guess I am. He's been so darned good to me, and I know he cares about me. Somehow I feel disloyal even dating Tony, much less going off on a weekend trip with him.'

'Have you made any promises to Richard?'

'Oh, no. Anything but. In fact, I've gone out of my way to discourage him.'

'Do you love him?'

Stacey bit her lip, thinking. 'In a way I do,' she said slowly at last. 'He's a wonderful person, a fine man, and would make an ideal husband.'

Peggy cocked an eyebrow. 'But?'

Stacey had to smile. 'You're right,' she said, nodding. 'It's not good enough. It wouldn't even be fair to him.'

Peggy gave a snort of disgust. 'I should have your problems!' she exclaimed. 'But if you really want to know what I think, I'd say forget Richard and focus on this great new guy. It's obvious that's what you really want.'

*   *   *

Back in her own apartment, Stacey mulled over their conversation. Was Peggy right? Was she being foolish, not to mention several decades out of date, to hold back from doing what she really wanted to do? And what kind of commitment was it she was looking for? Did she even want to marry again?

She thought too of how patient Tony had been since their talk. If she was getting tired of restraint in their lovemaking, think how it must be telling on him! How much longer would he be patient? And to what purpose? He wanted her, she wanted him. What was the point of delaying something that was most likely going to happen anyway eventually? And if her mind should turn a little wistfully to thoughts of love, wasn't it time to put such fantasies away?

Then she made up her mind. Of course she'd go with him to the cabin in Vermont. How could she ever have hesitated for a moment? And she'd tell him tonight, before she had a chance to dwell on it another minute and change her mind again.

But when she crossed over and knocked at his door, he didn't answer. She tried again later that evening, but when he hadn't arrived home by ten o'clock, she gave up. It could wait until tomorrow.

The next morning she woke up with a sore throat, a little feverish and achy, probably from the soaking she'd got in yesterday's storm, and she prayed she wasn't going to come down with some bug, not now that she had the wonderful trip with Tony to look forward to.

It would have to be a weekend now that school had started again, but that shouldn't be a problem for

Tony. His time seemed to be pretty much his own. She'd have to decide what clothes to take with her, too. It would undoubtedly still be very cold in Vermont.

Although it was a relief to have that dilemma resolved, there still remained the problem of an apartment to be faced. Apparently the other members of the committee had at least done something while she'd been so preoccupied with Tony, and she wished she'd listened more closely to Peggy yesterday when she'd tried to fill her in on their meager progress.

As she showered and dressed she searched her mind for the details. Something about the corporation behind it. Then, just as she was about to give up, it came to her. Global Enterprises! That was it! The name rang a distant bell in her mind, but she couldn't recall where she'd heard it before.

In the kitchen, she stood at the window drinking her morning coffee and chewing thoughtfully on a piece of toast. The rain had let up, and a pale winter sun was glistening on the still wet pavement far below. Surely there must be something she could do on her own to make up for her being so remiss.

Then it came to her. Why not tackle them directly? Although she shrank from the prospect of confrontation, she really had nothing to lose.

She had a class that morning at eleven. It was now only eight-thirty. Plenty of time. She looked up the address in the enormous Manhattan directory. They had offices in the Global Building, no less, on Madison Avenue.

An hour later, Stacey found herself sitting in an enormous and luxuriously-furnished foyer, forty stories up, waiting to speak to someone—anyone—in charge of the company's condominium project. After trailing from one Global office to another in search of the right department, she'd finally been directed to the Acquisition Section.

Before leaving home she'd called the chairman of the tenants' committee to tell him what she intended to do. While he wasn't very encouraging about the result, neither did he see any harm in trying. So here she was, all primed to beard the lions in their den, and she wasn't going to back down now that she'd come this far.

She'd already tackled the busy receptionist, who sat behind her desk eyeing Stacey suspiciously from time to time, and two secretaries, none of whom had any knowledge of the project at all.

Each setback, each attempt to foist her off on another underling, only fueled her determination, until finally, to her own utter astonishment, she had announced loudly and clearly to the last secretary that she'd pitch a tent in their blasted foyer or sleep on one of the couches if she had to, but she definitely was not going to leave until she spoke to someone in authority.

A further hour later, still firmly planted in her chair by the outer door, she saw two men come out of the inner office, one of them clearly distraught, his eyes glazed, the other grim-faced. On their way out they had to pass close by her, and stopped for a moment while the first man lit a cigarette with shaking fingers.

'I warned you it would be pointless,' his companion remarked dryly. 'The man is solid rock when it comes to business.'

'I know, I know,' the first man replied. 'I just thought if I brought you along, as legal representative, my position might be a little stronger.'

The other man shook his head. 'I explained all that weeks ago. He's perfectly within his legal rights to disband your company. Global owns it now, after all.'

Just then, a pleasant-looking, highly-yuppified young man came striding from the nether reaches toward her, a wide smile on his face, his hand outstretched. As he approached Stacey rose slowly to her feet and gave him a hopeful look.

'Ah, Miss Sinclair,' he said, flashing her a mouthful of even white teeth. 'I'm Daniel Masters. What can I do for you today?'

Stacey took his hand, gave it a token shake, then dropped it. 'I want to see the person in charge of your company's condominium conversion project,' she stated firmly.

'Well, perhaps I can help you. Just what is it you wanted to know?' He spread his hands in a gesture of fake regret. 'Although I'm afraid that project has been finalized and there really isn't anything to discuss. You do understand?'

'No,' she said. 'I don't understand. And it's far from finalized, Mr Masters.'

'Oh, but I think you'll find it is,' he said in a smug voice.

'Well, think again,' she rejoined tartly. 'I represent the committee in charge of fighting the project, and if you really are in charge of it, you must realize it hasn't gone through.'

The smile on the man's face faded. 'That's only a temporary condition, believe me. My understanding is that it's only a matter of time before the court makes its final decision.'

She eyed him carefully. 'You're not in charge of it at all, are you?'

'Well, not exactly.'

'Then who is? He's the one I want to talk to.'

Mr Masters gave her a look of disdain. 'I'm afraid that person is not available to discuss anything...'

Just then there was a commotion from the inner office; a loud masculine voice raised in anger. 'Masters! Where the hell is Masters?'

The young man blanched perceptibly, turned around and scurried toward the voice. 'Coming, Mr Devereux,' he called anxiously.

Stacey stared blankly at the man's fast-retreating back. Mr Devereux? Could it be? Then all the pieces began to fit together. Of course, it had to be. Just then she caught a glimpse of a tall, dark man, his face like thunder, with Mr Masters cowering before him, and her conclusion was confirmed. It was Tony.

With the speed of light, she turned tail and ran as fast as she could before he spotted her, out of the reception room, into the corridor and down to the bank of elevators, where she punched frantically at the 'down' button. When the elevator came, she dashed inside and leaned up against the far wall, her heart pounding in her ears, watching as the doors slid slowly closed.

Even though it seemed her whole world had suddenly collapsed around her, somehow Stacey got through that day. Numbed by the shock of her discovery, she managed to sit through her class without hearing one word, then put in her regular afternoon at the office, blindly going through the motions, grateful that at least Richard wasn't there.

As the hours ticked by her hurt at Tony's deception gradually turned into a simmering anger, a deep sense of betrayal, and, by the time she left the office at five o'clock, an explosive rage. As objectionable as she'd found Daniel Masters, Tony's treatment of him had given her the shivers.

Luckily she didn't have a class that night, and she was determined to confront him the minute she got home, tell him exactly what she thought of his underhand double-dealing.

On the bus going home she rehearsed her speech, every scathing comment she could think of, and as soon as she arrived at her building, before she could lose her momentum, she marched straight to Tony's door, pressed her finger on the bell and kept it there.

Finally she heard footsteps on the other side and an angry male voice call out angrily, 'All right! I'm coming!'

When he flung the door open his expression was ominous. He'd obviously just got out of the shower. His hair was still damp and all he had on was a hastily-donned pair of worn blue jeans. His feet were bare, and a small rivulet of water ran down the center of his bare chest.

'Oh,' he said, his expression softening. 'It's you.'

'May I come in?' she said, in a low, tense voice.

'Sure,' he replied, holding the door open for her.

She stood there stiffly in the bare living-room, her hands clenched into fists at her sides. She'd never been inside his apartment before. Now she didn't even bother to examine it, except to note that the only personal touch seemed to be a silver-framed photograph of an older couple on one table—his parents, no doubt.

'What's up?' he said in a puzzled voice, coming up behind her.

She whirled around to face him, her eyes flashing fire. 'You rat!' she exploded. 'You—you——' Words failed her.

'Hey, hold on,' he protested. 'What's wrong?'

She lifted her chin and put her face up to his. 'I'll tell you what's wrong!' she sputtered. 'I went to the Global office today, to try and argue our case, and I saw you there.'

Instantly a deep red flush washed over his face. He rubbed a hand over the back of his neck and stood there without speaking, frowning down at the floor. His silence only enraged her further.

'You lied to me!' she shouted. 'You tricked me! You only came here to spy on us, and for all I know the only reason you came on to me so slickly was to find out what the opposition was up to.' She curled her lip and gave him a look of utter contempt. 'All this time you've been wining and dining me you've been plotting behind my back to take my apartment away from me!'

Still he remained silent.

'Well?' she cried, stamping her foot. 'Haven't you?'

She was on the verge of tears by now, and even in her enraged state dimly perceived that a good part of her distress came from the painful fact that she was losing a man she'd come to care for a great deal, even to trust. That only made her angrier, however, and even more determined not to display any sign of weakness in front of him.

Finally he heaved a deep sigh, and lifted his head to give her a long look, his expression grave. 'I suppose you might interpret it that way,' he said. He tried out a weak smile. 'Although there's a big difference between a lie and withholding part of the truth.'

'Oh, please!' she drawled sarcastically. 'Spare me the nit-picking philosophical fine points. You knew how troubled I was about losing my apartment, and all along you were the mastermind behind the whole rotten business.'

'Well, hardly that,' he said equably. 'It wasn't my decision, at least not entirely. When the company made plans to turn these apartments into condominiums, I only came here to look the place over.'

A little ray of hope rose within her. 'So the final decision is yours?' she asked.

'Well, in a way.'

'So it's not actually all decided yet?'

'Yes, it is,' he replied quickly. 'Otherwise we wouldn't have sent that letter to the tenants.'

'But you could change all that if you wanted to?'

'Well, my opinion would carry some weight, yes.'

Her mind raced furiously. There might still be some hope after all. If Tony had come to live in Hannah's old apartment *after* the company sent the letters, that could only mean they weren't that sure of their ground. Perhaps they wanted him to test the tenants' reaction, see how far they'd go to fight the conversion.

'And what have you decided?' she asked at last, in a tight, strained voice.

He didn't say anything for a few moments, then sighed and gave her a regretful look. 'I'm afraid I haven't changed my mind, Stacey. I'm sorry, but it's a losing proposition.'

She searched his face for some sign of weakening, but all she saw there was a hard implacable expression, the eyes closed-in, the jaw set and unyielding, and she suddenly went limp inside, all the energy fueled by her anger draining away.

'Well, then,' she said at last in a shaky voice, 'I guess there's nothing more for us to say to each other.' She began to walk slowly toward the door. As she passed by him she gave him one last look. 'You know,' she said sadly, 'what you're doing is bad enough, but the fact you didn't tell me makes it a thousand times worse.'

He reached out and put a hand on her arm. 'Listen, Stacey,' he said in a low voice. 'I really am sorry that you had to find out this way. I know I should have told you myself, but somehow it never seemed like the right time, and I just delayed too long. I guess I was afraid it might prejudice you against me, and I'd come to care a lot about you. I only hope it won't make any difference to our relationship.'

Stunned by the arrogance of the man, she simply gave him a deeply pitying look. 'You can't be serious!' she said with feeling. 'How could I have any kind of relationship with a man who's taking away my home?'

'But it's not like that,' he said in an urgent tone. 'For God's sake, don't make me into some Simon Legree, who's going to put women and children out on the street without a roof over their heads. That's not fair.' He gave her a little shake. 'Look, I can loan you the money for the down payment. I'll *give* it to you.'

'I see,' she said with a scornful smile. 'You want to buy me, is that it? You provide the money and then we hop gaily into bed.'

'Oh, come on!' he said, growing angry himself now. 'Do you really believe I have to pay for favors from women?'

Looking at all that expanse of tanned muscular flesh before her, Stacey wavered. Of course he didn't. But it was too late to back down now.

'Well,' she said with a sniff, 'it sounded very much like it.'

'Take my word for it,' he said wryly. 'The money would be a gift—or a loan, if you'd prefer. No strings attached either way.' He held his hands up, palms forward, as though to demonstrate his claim.

Stacey only gave him another withering look. 'If you know me at all by now,' she said loftily, 'then you know I'd never take money from you, strings or no strings. You of *all* people!' she added scornfully.

'All right, forget the money. I'll help you find another place to live, one you can afford. The company owns several other buildings. I'm certain I can come up with something.'

'And what about the other tenants?' she asked angrily. 'What about Gladys Farmer down the hall, who can barely afford this place? Or Peggy Connors downstairs, just getting by on a teacher's salary?'

'And what about my company's shareholders?' he asked quietly. 'A lot of them are elderly people, who count on making a profit from their investment for security in their old age. If we confined our operations to bailing out companies that continue to operate at a loss, we'd soon be out of business. And, believe me, no one would come along to bail *us* out!'

By the time he was through, Stacey knew what she had to do. 'All right,' she said. 'You've made your point. I even see some justice to it. But we have our side too, and the same rules apply. I'm going to fight you on this, Tony, and I'm going to win.'

She sailed past him, her head held high, and made for the door again, but stopped when she heard him call to her.

'And what about us?'

She turned around and gave him a sickly-sweet smile. 'Us?' She shook her head and laughed bitterly. 'There is no "us", Tony. There never really was.'

CHAPTER SEVEN

IT WASN'T until Stacey was back in the safety of her own apartment, the door locked securely behind her, that reaction set in.

Heart pounding and shaking uncontrollably, she leaned back against the door, her eyes squeezed shut, breathing hard. After a moment she gradually slid to the floor, and sat there for a long time, her head resting on her knees, until finally the awful trembling stopped, her pulse-rate slowed, and she began to breathe more easily.

As she calmed down anger returned in full force. Somehow she had to beat Tony at his own game. The only problem was how. Scrambling to her feet, she went into the kitchen, then sat at the table for almost an hour, deep in thought, drinking cup after cup of black coffee, trying to come up with a plan of action.

Playing on his sympathy, his humanity, was out; that much was certain. He didn't have any. His was a cut-throat world. It was all he understood. Her only hope was to find a way to use his own weapons against him; to fight fire with fire.

Finally a small glimmer of an idea popped into her head. She couldn't do it alone. She'd have to have help.

Jumping to her feet, she ran to the telephone on the counter and dialed Peggy Connors' number.

'Peggy,' she said, when she answered. 'This is Stacey. Do you suppose you could get our tenants' group together tonight?'

'Tonight?' Peggy asked. 'Gosh, Stacey, I don't know. It's awfully short notice. Is it important?'

'I think I might have come up with an idea how to save our apartments, but I've got to have some co-operation. Is there a chance you can convince them all to come?'

'If you can do that,' Peggy breathed with feeling, 'I'll drag them out of bed if necessary. It's only eight o'clock. It shouldn't be a problem. Give me half an hour. I'll call you if I don't have any luck.'

During that half-hour Stacey managed to choke down a glass of milk, two pieces of toast and an apple, which was all her churning stomach could handle. Since she hadn't heard from Peggy, she assumed the meeting was on.

Out in the corridor, she glanced at Tony's door on her way to the elevator. All was silent behind it. Knowing it was childish and beneath her dignity, she made a face at it, then hurried on, feeling a little ashamed of herself. What if he'd come out and seen her? But then, did she really care?

True to her word, Peggy had assembled all the members of their committee together, and when Stacey saw them there, sitting in the living-room, their faces turned expectantly to her, her heart quailed within her. What if she'd only held out false hope to them? There was no reason to think her plan might work. But at least they'd be doing something, instead of just sitting back, like lambs led to the slaughter, waiting for the ax to fall.

She stepped inside and stood before them, surveying the little group. She was especially glad to see that Joan Fiorino was there. She was a key participant in her little plan.

She cleared her throat and plunged right in with no preliminaries. 'There are a couple of reasons I asked Peggy to get you all together tonight,' she began. 'The first is that I don't think the conversion is quite the sure thing we were led to believe. In fact, one of the top men at the company has already moved in here, apparently just to find out how much resistance to expect from us.'

They all began to talk at once, hurling questions at her and speculating on who the interloper might be. She *did* draw the line at publicly unmasking Tony. They might decide to lynch him. Not that he didn't deserve it. Finally she held up her hand for quiet.

'It doesn't matter who it is,' she said firmly, 'or how I found out. The point is there might be a way we can make them back down. For one thing, we have to stand firm.' She glanced at Jack Gardner, the lawyer in their midst. 'We definitely should keep up our legal delaying tactics as long as possible. How about it, Jack? Do you think you can gain us more time?'

'Oh, no question,' he replied with a grin. 'These things can drag on for months if we really put our minds to it.'

'Well, if my plan works, we won't need months,' she replied.

Then Joan Fiorino popped up. 'Well, come on, Stacey,' she said, with a touch of impatience. 'What is this great plan of yours?'

'Actually, Joan, it depends largely on you.'

The short, dark-haired woman widened her eyes and pointed at her chest. 'Me? What can I do?'

'Possibly nothing, but you're the only one of the group who has any newspaper connections.'

'But I'm only the gardening editor of a small local weekly!'

'Yes, but you must know someone—a reporter on one of the major dailies, for example, or even someone who *does* know one. What I have in mind is a publicity campaign. If we can get a newspaper interested in the case—you know, play on the public's sympathy—we just might make the conversion company back down in the end.'

They discussed the pros and cons for another two hours after that, and ended by everyone promising to do their best. Although Stacey didn't have a lot of hope that Joan could do anything, Gladys Farmer had a nephew who worked at the *Times*, and she promised she'd try to interest him in their plight.

When the meeting broke up and they all began straggling out the door back to their own apartments, Peggy put a hand on Stacey's arm, holding her back.

'So,' she said, when they were alone, 'aren't you going to tell me who the mystery man is?'

'Oh, Peggy, please don't ask. I admit he's probably not worth protecting, but I really don't want to be the cause of any bodily harm coming to him.'

'Well, I think I know anyway.'

'You do? How?'

'Oh, just call it instinct. You seemed to be pretty hot under the collar tonight on a purely personal level, and in my book that can only mean some man has dumped on you.' She heaved a heartfelt sigh. 'Why do such marvelous creatures have to be such rats?'

Stacey had to smile, but was still determined not to verify Peggy's suspicions. 'Well, I'll have to agree with you there, but it still doesn't prove anything. At this point I can't see that it really matters who he is. All I care about is keeping my apartment.'

'Well, your scheme is a shot in the dark, and I can see several flaws in it. But,' she added with a grin, 'it's just crazy enough to work.' Then she sobered again. 'But I'm still concerned about the possibility that there might be a personal element involved.'

'I don't see why,' Stacey replied stiffly.

Peggy shrugged. 'Well, he's a great-looking guy, a real hunk. He lives right across the hall from you. Could it be that things got out of hand, he hurt you in some way, and now you're trying to get even with him?'

Stacey searched her mind. 'No,' she said at last, in a firm voice. 'I'll admit we went out together a few times, but it never really amounted to anything remotely serious.'

'Oh, really?' Peggy drawled. 'And what about that trip to Vermont we discussed?'

Stacey flushed deeply. 'Oh, that,' she remarked, in an offhand tone. 'I decided not to go after all.' When she saw the dubious look on her friend's face, she realized she hadn't been as convincing as she'd hoped and hurried on. 'Honestly, Peggy, I have no personal ax to grind at all. I was shocked, of course, when I found out who he was, and angry that he hadn't told me sooner, but that's all. Besides, even if you were

right, I can't see that it would make any difference.
I mean, what we want is to keep our homes, isn't it?'

'Sure,' Peggy agreed hurriedly. 'I guess I just don't
want you to get carried away with something that
would end by spoiling your relationship with a perfectly good man. I mean, if this scheme of yours
works, he's going to be pretty upset, isn't he?'

'It's possible, I suppose, but what about what he's
doing to us? His company, anyway. It seems to me
he started the whole thing, and all in the name of
business. All I'm doing is trying to defend my rights,
and in a way he'd probably approve of. His pet motto
is "Business is business".'

Peggy laughed. 'Well, as long as you're sure. As I
say, it's just scatty enough to work.'

For the rest of the evening back in her own apartment,
and all through the following day, that talk with Peggy
preyed on Stacey's mind. She had to wonder if perhaps
she'd been very foolish, even childish, to let a purely
business situation spoil the budding personal relationship she'd been building with Tony before she'd
found out who he was.

Even though he had certainly withheld a piece of
information from her, and one that could have made
an enormous difference in their relationship, he hadn't
actually lied to her. And he'd said himself that the
reason he hadn't told her was that he was afraid of
losing her. Was she really going to toss that all out
the window just for the sake of an apartment?

In fact, now that she and the other tenants were
taking some concrete action to protect their interests,
the situation didn't loom quite so hopelessly, and

Tony's part in it began to seem less and less malevolent. However, by now the die was cast. There was no turning back. She knew he'd never come begging to her, and she certainly had no intention of backing down herself.

That very day, however, she was forced to face a more immediate and unsettling problem than the future of her apartment. The mild flu symptoms she'd felt coming on after her thorough drenching in the storm the other day had begun to escalate into alarming proportions.

She'd woken up that morning feeling a little more achy, her throat a little more sore, but had decided it wasn't serious enough to keep her home from work. Since she was on temporary status she only got paid for the actual hours she worked, and she needed every penny she could earn. She also had a class that night, and she didn't want to miss it.

By three o'clock that afternoon, however, she had serious doubts that she'd even be able to struggle through the rest of the day on the job until five, much less make it to school that evening. Her throat felt as though it were on fire, the sniffles had turned into a head full of cotton wool, every inch of skin on her body burned, and her head throbbed unmercifully.

Finally, by three-thirty, she knew that if she didn't leave now, she wouldn't even be able to get home on the bus by herself. She'd just have to tell Richard.

As she rose slowly from her chair, every muscle aching, a sudden wave of dizziness passed over her, so intense that her knees buckled under her and she actually blacked out for a moment. When she came to, she was slumped back down in her chair, her head resting on her desk.

'Stacey?' she heard someone call to her, the voice echoing, as though coming from a great distance.

With an enormous effort of will, she raised her head and blinked. Richard was standing on the other side of her desk, a frightened look on his face.

'Stacey, are you all right?'

She tried to smile at him to reassure him, but the effort made her jaw ache and she gave it up. 'No,' she croaked hoarsely. 'I don't think so.'

She sneezed loudly, groped for a tissue from the box on top of her desk, and blew her nose.

'Listen,' Richard went on in the same rather frantic tone, 'I think you'd better go home.'

She nodded miserably. 'I think you're right.'

He thought a minute. 'You'll never make it on the bus, you know.' He hesitated. 'I'll call you a taxi.'

'Yes,' she agreed wearily. 'Please.'

He gave her a sheepish look. 'I—uh—I'd drive you home myself,' he went on in a halting voice, 'but I'm up to my ears in this new account. You do understand, don't you?'

'Oh, yes.' At that point she would have agreed to anything.

'Well,' he said more briskly. 'I'll just see to it, then. You bundle up and I'll ask one of the girls to go with you down to the lobby. The cab should be waiting by the time you get there.'

He scuttled back inside his office, and in spite of her misery she had to smile. Poor Richard had a pathological horror of illness, and, although she knew his concern for her was genuine, she also knew he wouldn't get anywhere near anyone who might infect him with their germs.

She did manage to wobble to her feet and stay there this time. Somehow just the idea that she really was getting out of there gave her the impetus she needed. She fumbled awkwardly into her coat, picked up her handbag, and stood by her desk waiting for the promised help to arrive.

In a moment one of the file-clerks appeared, a sturdy, sensible-looking young girl named Janet. She took one look at Stacey, then hurried to her side, grasped her firmly by the arm and started leading her slowly down the hall.

'Gosh, Stacey,' she said as they went. 'You look terrible.'

'Thanks a lot, Janet,' she replied, forcing out a smile. 'But I couldn't possibly look worse than I feel.'

Halfway down the corridor she suddenly remembered a rather important message she'd forgotten to give Richard. She stopped short and turned around. He was standing at the door to his office, a safe twenty or thirty feet away from her. When she saw him smile weakly at her, and raise a hand to waggle his fingers in farewell, she thought, Oh, bother his stupid message, and turned to continue on down the hall.

The taxi was waiting for her at the curb in front of the building. It was chilly outside, and Stacey began to shiver, even in her heavy woolen coat. Janet bundled her inside, then leaned over her for a moment, gazing at her with a worried frown on her rather blunt features.

'Are you sure you'll be all right on your own?' she asked. 'I could come with you, if you'd like.'

'No. Thanks anyway, Janet, but I'll be all right now,' Stacey assured her truthfully. Just getting out of that stuffy, confining office had already made her feel better. 'And I don't want you to catch my bug, whatever it is.'

'Oh, that!' Janet exclaimed, with a contemptuous wave of her hand. 'I'm not worried about your bug.' Then she gave Stacey a conspiratorial grin. 'Not like some I could mention. Men!' she added with feeling.

Stacey smiled and nodded. 'Right. I know what you mean.'

'Well, then,' Janet said. 'I'd better get back to the salt-mine. The taxi's all paid for, compliments of Richard. Call me if you need anything.'

'Thanks again, Janet. I'll be fine. A hot bath, a cup of tea and a warm bed are all I need.'

'And chicken soup,' Janet rejoined with a grin. 'Don't forget the chicken soup. My mother's cure-all.'

Stacey nodded solemnly. 'Right. Lots of chicken soup.'

Once safely ensconced in her own apartment, the bath taken, the tea drunk, she did feel marginally better. At least not quite as rocky as she had at the office. She searched her cupboards for chicken soup—*any* kind of soup for that matter—but couldn't find any. Nor did she feel like getting dressed again and going out to shop.

Actually, she wasn't that hungry anyway, just weak and achy. She went into the bathroom and choked down two aspirin. As she passed through her bedroom she gazed longingly at the inviting-looking bed. What she really needed was sleep. However, if she ever got into that bed, she was afraid she'd never get up in time for her class that night.

She trudged wearily back into the kitchen to make another pot of tea, and as she stood there at the stove waiting for the kettle to boil a wave of self-pity passed over her, so intense that it brought tears to her eyes. She'd never make it to class that night. She was going to lose her apartment. She'd already lost the man she loved. Was life really worth living?

The screeching whistle of the boiling kettle broke into her dismal thoughts, and she gave herself a little shake. So she'd miss her class; so she felt rotten. It wasn't the end of the world. She'd been through worse times and come out of it intact.

Still, as she stirred a heaped spoonful of sugar into her strong tea, she felt a sudden overpowering urge to call her mother. She wouldn't whine or complain or beg for sympathy, she assured herself as she dialed her parents' number. She just wanted to hear the sound of her mother's voice.

To her utter dismay, however, the moment that warm, familiar voice came through the wires, she immediately burst into tears. She tried to stifle the sobs, but obviously failed.

'Stacey!' she heard her mother cry in alarm. 'Darling, what is it?'

'Oh, Mother,' she finally managed to choke out. 'I'm so sorry. It's really nothing, and the last thing in the world I wanted to do was upset you.'

'But, darling, tell me!'

'Oh, I've just picked up some kind of bug, and I felt so rotten I had to come home from work.'

'Well, shall I come down there to take care of you?'

'Oh, no!' Stacey replied quickly. She laughed lightly. 'I just need a day or two to rest, then I'll be fine. I'm pretty healthy, you know, thanks to all those vitamins you forced down my throat when I was a child.'

'Well, if you're sure. What are your symptoms?'

Stacey told her about her aching head and sore throat and stopped-up nose, trying to minimize them as far as she could. 'So you see,' she ended up, 'it's just a cold, or a light case of flu.'

'The best thing for you is bed,' her mother said, in exactly the same tone of voice she'd used when Stacey was a little girl. 'Keep warm, drink plenty of liquids, and take all the chicken soup you can manage. And if you don't feel any better by tomorrow, call the doctor.'

'Yes, Mother,' Stacey replied meekly.

'And no nonsense about going back to work or attending classes until you're feeling completely well again.'

'No, Mother.'

'And don't answer the doorbell or the telephone. You call me when you feel able. I won't even try to get in touch with you. Now, promise me you'll do what say?'

'Yes, Mother.'

They said goodbye then, and Stacey smiled as she replaced the receiver. Leave it to her mother to know just how to handle her. And she was right. She'd just have to miss her class tonight. The idea of bed sounded better all the time. She unplugged the telephone, then went back into her bedroom and crawled under the covers.

* * *

When she awoke it was pitch-dark outside, and she could hear the heavy patter of rain beating against the bedroom window. She glanced at the luminous dial of the clock beside her bed. Nine o'clock! She'd slept for five hours!

She also felt much worse. The effects of the aspirin and the tea and the talk with her mother had worn off completely, and she knew she was developing a raging fever. With a heroic effort, she dragged herself out of bed, stumbled to the bathroom, gulped down more aspirin, then fell back into bed again.

From then on, she seemed to hover between fitful, feverish sleep and painful reawakening, when she'd just managed to get to the bathroom and back. Food was out of the question. By now her stomach was lurching violently, on top of all her other symptoms. What she wanted was to die, just close her eyes and never wake up again to that dreadful aching.

The bedclothes were unpleasantly damp by now, but she was in such a daze she hardly noticed it. Occasionally, as she drifted in and out of her fitful sleep, she thought she could hear the distant sound of knocking at the door, but her mind was so fuddled from fever that she ignored it.

In her more lucid moments, it didn't take her long to panic over her situation. Here she was, all alone, with no one to help her. There wasn't a doctor in New York who would make housecalls. Richard was useless. Peggy, or her mother, or even Janet, would probably come to help her if she asked them to, but what was the point of infecting them?

She'd either get well or she'd die, and at that point she really didn't care which.

She had no idea of the time, or even what day it was. Except for her intermittent expeditions to the bathroom, where she was would gulp down aspirin and what seemed like gallons of water, she simply lay in bed, not really sleeping, but not fully conscious either. Sometimes the sky outside her bedroom window was dark, sometimes light. It made no difference.

Then, at some point, she became vaguely aware of a presence in the room, only dimly perceived in her somewhat comatose state. There was a cool cloth pressed to her burning forehead, an arm supporting her head, water being forced between her parched lips.

She blinked her eyes open, but the room was so dark that all she could make out was a bulky shape leaning over her. Had someone called a doctor? Had Richard overcome his phobia about germs? Had her mother simply taken matters into her own hands and made the trip down to nurse her?

She didn't much care. She closed her eyes and drifted off to sleep again.

Then, all of a sudden, after a truly terrible night, her fever raging, her sheets soaked with perspiration, she woke up with the certain knowledge that the worst had passed. She felt limp and weak as a kitten, but the awful aching was gone and her skin no longer felt as though it was burning up.

She opened her eyes to a pale sunlight streaming through the window. Glancing at the clock beside her bed, she saw that it was eight o'clock. It must be morning. But what morning? She tried to think. It had been on Thursday that she'd had to leave work, but everything that came after was a blank.

With a supreme effort, she raised herself up on her elbows, thinking to get out of bed to turn on a radio or find the morning newspapers that had undoubtedly collected during her illness, but stopped short when a commanding voice suddenly barked out from the direction of the hall door.

'Just what do you think you're doing?'

She turned to see Tony walking toward the bed, a stern expression on his face. She shook her head and blinked. It must be a hallucination. She was still feverish. Then, when the apparition didn't disappear, she knew it had to be him. Buy why?

By now he was leaning over the bed, his arm around her shoulders, easing her head back down on the pillow. He put a glass of water to her lips, but she made a face and turned her head away.

'Tony?' she asked, totally bewildered. 'Is it really you?'

He nodded. 'In the flesh. Now, drink this.'

As she began to sip obediently she felt his hand on her forehead. 'Good,' he said. 'Your fever's broken. Are you hungry?'

'Not really.'

'You will be.'

'How long have you been here? And how did you get in?'

'We can talk about that later. Do you feel up to a bath? I'd like to get your sheets changed.'

She gave him a weak smile. 'It sounds heavenly.'

'Good. I'll run a tub for you.' He straightened up and stood staring sternly down at her. 'And you're not to try to get out of bed, mind, until I come back to help you. We don't want you collapsing on the floor again, do we?'

He turned on his heel and disappeared into the adjoining bathroom, and in a moment she could hear water running. She lay back and closed her eyes. She had no idea why he was here or how he had even found out she was sick, but she wasn't going to argue with him about it now. He could very well have saved her life, and she was perfectly content simply to let him take charge.

When he came back a few minutes later she had already risen to a sitting position, and was about to get out of bed, but when she saw the warning look on his face, she decided against it after all. Instead, she waited until his arms came around her, lifting her up, and allowed him to carry her into the bathroom without a murmur of protest.

'Now,' he said, setting her down beside the fragrant, steaming tub. 'Can you manage on your own, or do you need help?'

'Oh, I think I can manage.'

'Well, I'll just go change your bed, then. I'll leave the door open a crack and won't be out of earshot. Call me if you get in any trouble.' He pointed at the counter. 'I found a clean nightgown in your dresser.'

When he was gone she stripped off her sodden nightgown, then very slowly and cautiously stepped into the tub. It felt heavenly, filled with her favorite bath-oil, and she leaned her head back with a contented sigh. After she'd soaked for a good ten minutes, she began to realize that if she didn't get out, she'd fall asleep in the cooling water.

As she dried off she did hazard one brief look in the bathroom mirror, and what she saw there so horrified her that she vowed not to do it again until she was entirely recovered. Her hair hung to her shoulders in dank strands, her face was white and gaunt, and there were dark circles under her eyes.

There was a hairclip lying on the counter, and she did at least manage to pin the most straggly locks back from her face. Not much of an improvement, but by now she was feeling so weak from her exertions that she'd lost all concern about her appearance anyway.

Dressed in her fresh nightgown, she tottered toward the door, but when her knees started to buckle she stood there for a moment, hanging on to the counter, her eyes closed, waiting for the sudden weakness to pass. Then she felt herself being picked up again and deposited in her bed again between blessedly clean sheets.

As Tony tucked the covers up around her chin she lay back on the pillows with a sigh of relief, and immediately felt herself drifting off to sleep. The last thing she remembered before she fell into unconsciousness was the feel of cool lips pressed against her forehead.

The next time she awoke it was growing dark outside. Had she really slept that long? She raised up and sniffed the air. Was that chicken soup she smelled? And had Tony really been there earlier? Or was it all part of a feverish mirage?

The answer came quickly enough when Tony himself appeared at the door, carrying a tray.

'Ah,' he said. 'I thought it was about time you woke up, Sleeping Beauty.'

She had a sudden vision of the sight she'd seen in the mirror earlier. 'Oh, right,' she replied dryly, running a hand over her tumbled hair. 'Every man's dream!'

He set the tray on the table beside her bed and, chin in hand, gazed down at her with satisfaction. 'Well, I must say, I've seen you look better. However, you do have a little more color than you did this morning.' He reached out a hand and placed it on her forehead. 'And the fever's stayed down. That's good. Now, how about some...?'

'I know,' she said with a weak laugh. 'Chicken soup.'

He smiled at her. 'How did you ever guess? Feel up to eating it yourself? Or shall I help you?'

She raised herself up, glad to find she could make it on her own. 'I think I can do it myself,' she replied. 'It smells heavenly. I don't think I've ever been so hungry in my life.'

He placed the tray down on her lap. 'I'll leave you to it, then,' he said. 'I just put some coffee on and had better see to it. I'll be back shortly.'

She finished every bit of the soup, as well as the dish of cheese and crackers and the glass of milk also on the tray, and when she'd finished she leaned back with a sigh of contentment. No meal had ever tasted so good to her.

Just then Tony came back, carrying two steaming mugs. He handed one to her and sat down on the chair beside the bed.

'Tony, I don't even know what day it is,' she said.

'Monday,' was the prompt reply.

'Then I've been sick for four days?'

'Sounds about right.'

'But I still don't know what you're doing here.'

He took a long swallow of coffee, then set his mug down on the table and leaned back in his chair. 'Well, on Friday I noticed you hadn't picked up your morning newspaper and, like a good neighbor, I rang the bell to see if something might be wrong. When you didn't answer, and the next day another paper was lying there, I got the super to let me in.'

'Then you've been here since Saturday?'

He nodded. 'On and off,' he replied crisply. He rose to his feet and reached for her mug. 'Do you want more coffee? Or more soup?'

'No, thanks.' She thought a minute, then gazed up at him, a puzzled look on her face. 'But why, Tony?' she asked. 'Why did you do all this for me, especially after——?' She broke off as she recalled that last unpleasant encounter with him.

He shrugged. 'Why not? Now, if you're sure you don't need anything else, I'd better go wash the dishes. Try to get some sleep. Best thing for you right now.'

She was feeling too weak to argue with him just then, but she made up her mind that as soon as she'd had a short nap, she'd tackle him on the subject again. The way they had parted at their last meeting, when she'd been so angry at him for deceiving her over his ownership of the apartment building, she would never have expected him to speak to her again, much less nurse her through an illness.

Somehow now, realizing what he'd done for her, and, more, just the fact of his presence in her life again, made the whole condominium affair fade into insignificance.

CHAPTER EIGHT

STACEY'S recovery was slow, but steady. The high point was getting her hair washed, over Tony's strenuous objections, the very next day. She also called Richard, to tell him she'd be away from the office most likely for the rest of the week, and her mother, to reassure her that she was all right.

'Oh, I'm so glad, darling,' her mother said. 'I've been so worried about you down there all alone.'

'Well, not quite alone, Mother,' she replied. 'A neighbor very kindly came to see me through the worst of it.'

'Well, dear, you're lucky to have such a thoughtful neighbor, especially in New York.'

Stacey had to smile. To her mother, New York was the modern equivalent of Sodom and Gomorrah rolled into one.

For the most part, however, she slept. Her appetite gradually returned, and Tony always seemed to know just what delicacy would tempt her. She soon graduated from chicken soup, and by Tuesday evening was enjoying a rich stew. For the occasion she had put on a robe and slippers to join him at the kitchen table.

'That was wonderful, Tony,' she said as she swallowed the last delicious bite. 'Don't tell me you whipped it up yourself?'

'Well, no, as a matter of fact, I didn't,' he replied with a smile. 'There's a nice little restaurant down the block that has a takeaway service. But,' he added firmly, 'I can cook, believe it or not, and as soon as you feel well enough I'll demonstrate my culinary skills for you.'

He got up to pour out their after-dinner coffee, and she watched him, so tall, so confident, making himself so much at home in her tiny kitchen. Lord only knew what luxuries he was used to.

'You know,' she said, when he'd sat back down. 'I still can't figure out why you've gone to all this trouble for me.'

'Ah, but I explained that. I was just being a good neighbor. Wouldn't you have done the same for me?'

She laughed. 'I honestly don't know.' Then she sobered. 'I hope so. Anyway, I think I can manage pretty well on my own now. I really should be thinking about getting back to work.'

'There's no hurry about that. Don't rush into anything. You still need a good rest.'

'Well, I also need to earn a living.' She hesitated for a moment, then asked lightly, 'What about you? Don't you have business of your own to take care of?'

He leaned back in his chair. 'Oh, my business can wait.' He paused for a moment, then went on. 'However, since you raised the subject, I think we need to get a certain issue settled, now that you're feeling better.'

'Yes,' she said. 'I agree.'

'I guess the best way to begin is to ask you if you still see me as some kind of monster set on taking homes away from widows and orphans.'

'Well, you'll have to admit it did seem that way.'

'Perhaps you're right. Before coming here to live, seeing the actual individuals who would be hurt by the conversion, it simply seemed like good business practice. As I mentioned to you in one of our stormier discussions, my company is not a charitable institution. We are responsible to our stockholders, and if we don't show a profit, they're harmed.'

'Yes,' she said. 'I understand that. But *my* immediate concern is to keep my own home, something I can afford, and that goes for the other tenants, who will have nowhere to go if they're forced out of here. I just can't see any solution at all.'

'There's *always* a solution,' he stated firmly. 'The world of business is based solidly on the art of compromise.'

She gave him a quick look. 'I see. Then you do think it's possible to find a way out so that we——' She broke off and dropped her eyes to her plate, reddening at what she'd been about to say.

When she felt his hand cover hers she glanced up at him. He was smiling at her, and there was no mockery in the bright blue eyes this time, but a glow that warmed her heart.

'So that we can pick up where we left off?' he inquired gently. 'Is that what you were about to say?'

'Something like that,' she murmured. But immediately it occurred to her that she had no idea what their old status had actually been. He could be right; there might be a solution to the business conflict that had driven them apart, but that still left them exactly where they'd been before—still at cross-purposes, with Tony apparently unwilling to commit beyond the present moment.

She sighed deeply at the thought, and felt his hand tighten on hers. 'Come on,' he said in a teasing voice. 'It can't be as bad as that.' He released her hand, then rose abruptly from his chair and came around the table to stand behind her. 'It'll work itself out,' he said softly, putting his hands on her shoulders and kneading them gently.

A slow warmth began to steal through her at the touch, and when she felt his cheek come to rest against hers, the day's stubble rasping slightly, and drank in the clean scent of him, she knew she had to believe him, to hope that it really would be all right.

He placed his lips briefly at the corner of her mouth, then slowly, with a long, lingering gesture, he withdrew his hand from her shoulder. 'Sleep well,' he said softly. 'I'll look in on you tomorrow.'

The next morning Stacey awoke feeling almost normal again; there was just a little weakness in her legs as she showered and dressed. She was also ravenously hungry.

By the time she'd dressed and combed her clean hair out, it was almost nine o'clock. Tony had said he'd look in on her today, and since he'd been showing up early during his nursing stint, she decided to surprise him and fix breakfast herself today.

Glowing with anticipation at the prospect of seeing him soon, and humming a little under her breath, she put the coffee on and set the table for two. Just as she was taking the bacon and eggs out of the fridge she heard his key in the lock. Her heart gave a great leap, then started pounding erratically.

'Well,' he said from the doorway. 'Just what do you think you're doing out of bed?'

She turned slowly around. He was standing there, hands resting lightly on his hips, and scowling darkly.

'I'm fixing breakfast for us,' she replied with a smile. 'Are you hungry?'

He came walking toward her. 'It looks as though you won't be needing my services much longer. Are you sure you're up to this?'

'Positive. Now, sit down at the table while I do the work for a change. You've already done enough for me, coming around every day the way you have been. Anyway, I do want you to know how grateful I am for all you've done for me. To tell you the truth, I didn't know you had it in you.'

'Well, you really never knew me very well, did you?'

She gave a dry laugh. 'No, I didn't. How could I, when you kept so much hidden from me?'

He narrowed his eyes at her. 'We're not going to start in on that again, are we?'

'Oh, I'm not accusing you of anything,' she said, dishing up plates of bacon and eggs and setting them down on the table. 'I'm not even angry about it any more. In fact I'm even willing to admit that your shareholders probably have as much right to a return on their investment as we tenants do to keep our homes.' She poured out the coffee, then sat down across from him. 'I'm just pointing out that I could hardly have come to know you well when you concealed the most important fact about yourself.'

He tilted his chair back and gave her a long look, his expression grave. 'Is that what you think?' he asked quietly. 'That the fact I work for the company that owns this building is the most important thing about me?'

'Well,' she faltered, suddenly unsure of her ground. 'I certainly did at the time.'

'And now?' he asked, picking up his fork and tucking into his breakfast.

She dropped her eyes. 'Now I'm not so sure,' she murmured. 'As I say, you do have your side of it.'

They ate in silence for a while, each wrapped in their own thoughts. When Tony had chewed and swallowed the last bite, he braced his elbows on the table and leaned forward, holding her gaze in his.

'Does that mean you've given up casting me in the role of villain in the whole affair?'

She returned his look, held by those brilliant blue eyes. 'It wasn't so much that,' she replied at last. 'What really hurt was that you hid it from me.'

'Yes, I admit I did that. I also told you my reason for doing so. I knew how you'd react, and by then I didn't want to lose you.' He reached out and took her hand in his. 'You were the most important thing to have come into my life in a long, long time.'

He frowned slightly then, and gazed past her into the distance, as though his thoughts were taking him into territory long-forgotten, where she could not follow him. Watching him, Stacey had to wonder what that last statement really meant. Just how important was she to him? She remained silent, holding her breath and waiting, certain there was more to come.

'When I lost my parents so suddenly,' he went on at last, 'I had the crazy idea that they'd let me down somehow, that the two people I trusted most and believed I could count on forever had just disappeared and left me all alone.'

'But, Tony,' she said softly, deeply touched at the admission of weakness from such a strong man. 'They died.'

He waved a hand in the air. 'Oh, I knew how ridiculous that idea was, even at the time, and I certainly don't have it any more.' A shadow crossed his face, darkening his fine features, and his hand tightened on hers. 'But since losing them I've never quite got over the feeling that caring deeply about anyone at all means leaving oneself vulnerable to pain.' Then he smiled. 'But you know all about loss yourself, don't you? You must have had similar feelings when your husband was killed.'

'Yes,' she murmured, but she knew in her heart that there was really no comparison. She and David had been married such a short time and had been so young. Certainly her feelings for him were vastly different from the way she felt about Tony.

Then a cold chill ran down her spine as she realized just how powerful those feelings had become, that she was hopelessly in love with him, especially after the tender care he'd taken of her during her illness. But at the same time she could also see the obstacles that were in the way. And not only the battle over the building. Just because Tony had admitted she was important to him it didn't mean he was any more ready for love, for commitment, than he'd ever been.

'Penny for them,' she heard him say.

She looked up at him and gave him a quick smile. 'They're not worth even that much.'

'You do know what I've been trying to tell you, don't you?' he said.

'Not exactly,' she replied cautiously.

He leaned closer to her and ran a hand up her arm, underneath the sleeve of her robe. 'I'm saying that I want us to pick up where we left off. I know there are difficulties. We'll have to get this damned condo situation straightened out first. What do you say? Is it worth another try to you?'

'Yes,' she said, without hesitation. 'It is.'

'Then how about trying again for our trip to Vermont?' he said in a low voice. 'When you're entirely recuperated, that is.'

Her mind raced. Was she ready for this? Everything had happened so fast her head was swimming. She gave him a questioning look, as though searching for an answer in the steady blue eyes, the grave expression. But he was obviously not going to help her out, or pressure her, was leaving it entirely up to her.

'All right,' she finally blurted out. 'Yes. I'd like to go.'

He nodded with satisfaction. 'Good.' Then he rose from his chair. 'Now, I think it's time you got some rest. You're not entirely well quite yet. I'll check back with you later in the day.'

As he passed behind her chair he put his arms around her neck and dipped his head down to brush his lips lightly over her cheek. She leaned her head back against him in a gesture of surrender, and as his seeking mouth moved to hers one hand slid down to rest lightly on her breast. Then, with a quick intake of breath, he pulled it away.

'If you don't get well soon,' he said, in a hoarse voice, 'I won't answer for the consequences.' He straightened up, sighing heavily. 'Mind you don't overdo.'

'No, sir,' she replied happily.

'I've got a few things to take care of now,' he said, moving away from her. 'I've already put our account-ants and legal experts to work on our little problem, and I want to see what they've come up with.'

Somehow, she thought as she watched him go, she had the feeling that they'd darned well *better* have come up with something, or they'd have Tony to answer to. And she smiled to herself.

At five o'clock that afternoon the telephone rang. It was Peggy from downstairs, and she sounded breathless with excitement.

'Stacey!' she shouted. 'Have you seen the evening paper?'

'No, I haven't,' she replied, bewildered. 'I take the morning edition.'

'Well, by gosh, we did it!' Peggy crowed triumphantly.

'Did what?'

'Got a full-page spread about the conversion. You know, all us poor folk out on the streets because of the wicked wiles and heartlessness of big business. It's marvelous!' she rushed on. 'Photographs and every-thing. There's a great one of you as the instigator of the whole campaign.'

Stacey's mind raced. Should she feel gratified or appalled? She was glad that the committee had at-tained its goal, but, after what had been happening between her and Tony recently, she had the sinking feeling that she might just have cut her own throat.

'Well, that's great,' she finally managed to say in a feeble voice. 'I guess.'

'Well, you don't sound particularly overjoyed. After all, it *was* your idea.' Then she paused a moment. 'Uh, by the way, how are you feeling? Is your flu any better?'

'Yes, I'm on the mend.' She thought quickly. 'Listen, Peggy, I've got to go now. Thanks a lot for calling and letting me know.'

'Well, brace yourself. The paper wants to interview you as soon as you feel up to it.'

'Oh!' Stacey groaned. 'I don't know if I want to do that.'

'Well, I told the reporter you'd been sick. But, now that we have some publicity, I think we'd better capitalize on it if we want results—keep it alive in the public mind.'

'Yes. You're probably right. I'll think about it.'

Her heart pounding furiously, her head in a whirl, she hung up the telephone receiver, then stood there for a moment, trying to get her bearings, clear her mind, decide what to do.

Clearly she had to do something. The most important thing was to talk to Tony, explain to him how this had happened, before he saw the article. But first she had to read it for herself. She ran to the hall closet to get her coat and scarf, then stopped short in the midst of struggling into it.

What if he'd already seen it? Granted, it wasn't exactly screaming headlines, but it was something of interest to him and his company. Surely he would know about it by now. Then she'd just have to make him understand that the whole thing had been decided before her illness and their very tentative reconciliation.

She buttoned up the coat, tied a scarf hastily over her head, and made tracks for the corner newsstand.

Twenty minutes later she was back in her apartment, the newspaper spread out on the kitchen table, her head in her hands, groaning aloud periodically as she scanned the full-page spread.

It was far worse than she'd feared. Not only was her name featured prominently in the lead article as 'the fearless ringleader who spearheaded this campaign', which made her sound like the head of an underworld gang of thugs or a spy-ring, but somehow they'd got hold of Tony's name too! And, of course, cast him in the role of villain of the piece.

Mr Anthony Devereux, one of the highest of the high honchos at Global, has actually been living in the doomed building for some months now, no doubt plotting the massive takeover of these rent-controlled apartments, a move that will put many low-income tenants out on the street and most likely add to the city's already shameful problem of the homeless. So far, Mr Devereux has been unavailable for comment.

'Oh, no!' Stacey wailed aloud. How could they? And how had they got hold of Tony's name in the first place? Peggy! It had to be Peggy!

She jumped to her feet, ran to the telephone on the counter, and dialed Peggy's number. Tapping her foot impatiently, she listened to it ring—twice, five times, eight—until finally a breathless Peggy answered.

'Yes? Hello?'

'Peggy, it's Stacey.'

'Oh, Stacey. I just now came in the door. What can I do for you? Have you seen the article yet?'

'Yes. It's why I'm calling.'

'Great, isn't it?'

'Peggy, did you give them Tony's name?'

There was a short silence. Then, 'Well, uh, yes, as a matter of fact, I did,' came the stiff reply.

'Oh, Peggy, how could you? I never told you who he was. You can't make up things like that about another person and blab your guesswork to reporters. There is such a thing as the law of libel, you know. This could have serious repercussions.'

There was another silence, then Peggy's stiff voice came on the line again. 'Are you telling me that Tony Devereux has no connection with Global? That he's not here as their representative? Because if you are, I'd like to inform you that I checked with them before I gave the paper his name.'

'But Peggy...'

'And furthermore,' Peggy went on in an icy tone, 'as for any repercussions, is it really the legalities you're so worried about? If so, let me assure you that I said nothing that wasn't true. Or do you have a purely personal stake in all this?'

Stacey couldn't answer. All she could see was the collapse of all her high hopes regarding Tony, the wreckage of her entire life strewn at her feet. And now she'd antagonized Peggy, who'd been a good friend to her when she needed one.

'I'm sorry, Peggy,' she finally said lamely. 'I guess I'm still not entirely recuperated from my flu. It's just that it was such a shock to see my name, and Tony's, in print. Forgive me?'

'Well, all right,' came the grudging reply. 'Since you're pleading illness,' she went on in a more cheerful tone. 'And I'm sorry too. I suppose I should have checked with you first, but I was so darned excited when the opportunity came up to tell our story I just didn't think how it might affect you. After all, it's what you wanted, isn't it? I mean, it was your idea in the first place.'

'Yes, I guess you're right,' Stacey agreed with a sigh.

'Well, then, are we still friends?'

'Yes, of course.'

The rest of that day turned out to be a nightmare. It seemed the telephone never stopped ringing. Each time she answered it her heart burgeoned with hope that it would be Tony, but it always turned out to be someone else. Richard, the other tenants, even her mother. And, of course, and not least of all, the reporters, hungry for a more personal angle on their story.

Finally she'd had all she could take of explanations and replies to probing questions, and she unplugged the telephone. Even if Tony had tried to call her the line was always so busy he wouldn't have been able to get through.

She also still felt a little wobbly from her recent illness. All this excitement was wearing her down. What she needed was a nice long nap. But, before collapsing in bed, she had to give Tony one more try and see if he had returned to his apartment.

Twice already she'd opened her door to insistent knocking only to find a reporter standing there, shouting questions at her the moment she stuck her head out. On both occasions she'd spotted a man with a camera and a woman with a microphone across the hall, hanging around Tony's door.

Of course, she knew quite well that she wasn't really what they were interested in—or the fate of the apartment building. But Anthony Devereux was news, and the more dirt they could dig up about him the better.

It was no wonder he wasn't answering the telephone, but it was possible he was barricaded in his apartment, and she wouldn't rest easy until she gave it one more try.

She went to the door, unbolted and unlocked it as quietly as possible, then inched it open a crack, just wide enough to give her a limited view of the hallway. It seemed quiet and empty.

But when she pulled the door open wider and stuck her head out, immediately, from out of nowhere, a very determined-looking newswoman popped out of the shadows, pencil poised over a shabby notebook, the cameraman close behind her.

Uttering a startled little cry, Stacey pulled back, slammed the door shut and locked and bolted it securely. She could still hear the newswoman's insistent voice calling her from the other side.

It was hopeless. She might as well give up trying to reach Tony for now and take her nap. She felt utterly wiped out. She'd just have to wait until he contacted her—if he ever did.

When she woke up it was pitch-dark. She glanced groggily at the bedside clock, and could hardly believe her eyes. It was almost midnight!

She jerked herself bolt upright and switched on the light. Even though her empty stomach was growling, her first thought was for Tony. Perhaps by now he'd come home.

She jumped off the bed and ran straight to the front door. There was total silence on the other side, but she'd been fooled by that before. She pressed her ear against the door, but still couldn't make out a sound. Apparently even newspeople had to sleep some time.

Then, just as she was about to open it, she heard it—a slight sound, the soft snick of the door to Tony's apartment across the hall. It had to be him! Surely even those bloodthirsty newshounds wouldn't break into the man's apartment. If they had, she'd call the police.

Emboldened by that thought, she opened the door wide and stepped out into the hall. At that same moment Tony's door shut quietly. She marched across and knocked. No reply. She knocked again, more loudly.

'Who is it?' came a masculine voice, muffled, but instantly recognizable as Tony's.

'It's me, Stacey,' she replied softly.

In a moment she heard the click of the lock. The door opened. She gazed up at him, all ready to commiserate, apologize, explain, but at the sight of him she couldn't quite find the right words.

He was dressed in a suit and tie, and, although there
was a trace of dark stubble on his jaw, he looked as
bandbox-fresh and well-tailored as ever. Nor, to her
surprise, did he seem in the least harried or upset after
what must have been a most trying day. In fact he
was smiling at her, and somehow his composure made
her feel even more nervous and tonguetied than she
did already.

'Well,' he said, with the lift of one heavy black
eyebrow. 'You've managed to create quite a sensation
in today's Press. Congratulations.'

She gave him a dubious look. The smile was still
in place, but even in the glow of the dim light burning
at the far end of the hall she could tell there was no
amusement in it. His eyes were hooded so that they
appeared almost black, and his jaw was set in a firm
line.

'Well,' she began haltingly. 'That's what I wanted
to talk to you about.'

'Do you really think there's anything we have to
say to each other?' he asked in an even, almost con-
versational tone.

'Yes,' she replied firmly. 'I most certainly do.'

He cocked his head to one side, as though thinking
it over. 'All right,' he said, opening the door wider.
'Come inside, then, by all means. It might at least
afford me some amusement to hear your version of
events. God knows I could use a laugh right about
now.'

The living-room was as dimly lit as the hallway, but,
by some trick of fate, the neon light from the building
across the street flashed on just then, illuminating the
darker corners of the room.

She noticed then that there was a large leather valise and a smaller briefcase sitting just inside the door, over to one side. She turned around to face him. He was standing with his back to the door, his arms folded across his chest, gazing at her with a bland and totally inscrutable expression on his face.

She gestured toward the cases. 'Looks as though you've been packing,' she said lightly.

He nodded shortly. 'Yes. I'm leaving, of course. I just stopped by to pick up a few personal things.'

'But why?'

He laughed shortly and without humor. 'Well, obviously I can't stay here. Not with reporters haunting the place.'

'Well, that's why I came, to explain about that.' She gazed around wildly, searching for the words to make her case, to penetrate that defensive wall he had erected around himself. 'Do you suppose we could sit down?'

He hesitated, then nodded again. 'All right. Be my guest.'

Stacey went over to the couch by the window and perched on the edge. In a moment he followed her, took the chair across from her then leaned forward, his hands clasped between his knees, eyeing her thoughtfully.

'I just wanted to tell you,' she began haltingly, 'that all this fuss started before——' She broke off, unsure how to phrase the next bit.

'Before I barged in and fed you chicken soup?' he supplied with an unpleasant smile.

'Well, yes, that too.' She raised her chin. Clearly he wasn't going to help her out, and she began to wonder what she was doing here in the first place.

'But what else was there?' he asked in a reasonable tone. 'Now you're well again. You don't need my ministrations. And you've taken steps—quite clever ones, I might add—to get what you really wanted all along—to save your apartment.' He shrugged. 'It's all part of the game.' He leaned further toward her then, his eyes fixed on her. 'Just a word of warning, however, since you're new at it. You may have won this round, but don't count on winning the war.'

If he had slapped her she couldn't have felt more humiliated. All she could do was stare at him. The Tony she'd come to care for during the past several days had vanished. In his place was a hard man of business, who once again had become her mortal enemy.

'I see,' she said finally. She rose abruptly to her feet. 'Then I guess there's nothing more we have to say to each other.'

He got up and walked slowly over to her side. For several moments he merely stood there, looking down at her. She couldn't meet his eyes, but she could feel them boring into her. She knew she should just march past him, out the door, out of his life, but for some reason she felt paralyzed.

Finally he spoke. 'I trusted you, Stacey,' he said, in a low, quiet voice, and now she could hear the strain in it. 'More than I've ever allowed myself to trust another human being.'

She jerked her head up. Maybe there was still a chance he'd listen to her, let her explain. But by the

time her eye caught his the mask had come down
again. He turned swiftly, preceded her to the door
and opened it.

There was nothing left for her to do. Without a
word she went past him out into the hall. As she
crossed over to her own apartment she didn't look
back once, but before she let herself in she heard his
door close quietly.

Still numb from the crushingly disappointing encounter, she was just plodding heavily toward the
kitchen to make herself a cup of coffee when she heard
a sudden commotion coming from the hall. She
whirled around and ran to the door, opening it just
wide enough to see what was going on.

Out of nowhere, several reporters had barged in,
with the newswoman and her cameraman forming the
vanguard. They were surrounding Tony, who was
carrying the leather valise, the briefcase under one
arm. He simply stood there, his expression stern and
aloof, but with a thin smile on his face, apparently
relaxed and at ease as the woman shoved the microphone at him, the camera flashed and several voices
were raised at once.

Stacey watched, mute, spellbound, as Tony deftly
parried every question, even struck a pose for the
cameraman, holding up his briefcase and smiling
broadly. All the while he was inching toward the elevator, and when it arrived he stepped inside the car,
the gang following close after him until the doors slid
shut and he was lost from view.

Stacey felt stunned. Everything had happened so
fast that she couldn't think, couldn't quite grasp what
had happened. That very morning she'd been full of

delighted anticipation at the possibility of a bright future, one that included Tony Devereux as a somewhat unknown, but integral part. Now that dream was shattered, and for the life of her she couldn't figure out why. She'd meant well, but obviously had blundered badly, and as far as she could see there was no way she could get back what she had lost.

For the second time in her life Stacey took a sleeping-pill before falling into bed, from the supply her doctor had given her right after David's death. After tossing and turning for fifteen or twenty minutes, she finally felt a blessed numbness creeping into her tormented mind and drifted off into unconsciousness.

CHAPTER NINE

THE next morning Stacey awoke to an unholy racket coming from the direction of the hallway—loud voices, the sound of clanging metal, the whirr of a motor.

Cautiously she opened one eye. A bright ray of sunshine was streaming in through her bedroom window. She sat up in bed, straining her ears. The hubbub out in the hall continued, and she was immediately on-guard. It didn't *sound* like reporters, but one never knew. Better take a quick look.

Still a little groggy from the sleeping-pill she'd taken the night before, she got out of bed, slid her feet into her slippers, threw on a dressing-gown and, tying it around her waist as she went, walked quickly to the hall door.

When she opened it, the first thing she saw was that the door to Tony's apartment was standing ajar. The noise seemed to be coming from inside. Then, when a stout woman wearing an apron, a scarf tied over her head, appeared, pushing a vacuum cleaner before her, she realized that it must be the janitor service cleaning out Tony's apartment.

She picked up the morning paper and went back inside, closing the door behind her. So, he had left. Well, he'd said that was what he was going to do, and if she knew anything at all about the man it was that he usually did precisely what he said he would. She'd probably never even see him again.

Just then her stomach gave a loud rumble, and it dawned on her that she hadn't had anything to eat since noon yesterday. Eat first, she decided, making her way to the kitchen, and worry later.

As she wolfed down her orange juice, two scrambled eggs, a rather stale Danish pastry and two cups of strong coffee she skimmed through the morning paper, until finally, in the second section, she came upon a full-length photograph of Tony, obviously shot as he was leaving last night. He had on the same suit and tie and was carrying the same leather valise and briefcase.

She stared down at it, long and hard. He looked perfectly at ease, a quirky smile on his face, one hand raised as though in explanation—of *his* side of the matter, no doubt—and it didn't take long for her to work up a fine indignation of her own.

What business did he have getting so angry with her last night? She'd done nothing wrong, had betrayed no confidence. She had nothing to feel guilty about. All she'd wanted was to keep her home. She'd only played by his rules, and if they'd backfired on him, why that was his lookout, not hers. What he was really furious about was that she'd won, beat him at his own game, but he was too pig-headed to accept defeat gracefully.

Or had she actually won? She suddenly recalled his comment about winning a battle, not the war. There was still a lot to be done before it was over, more battles ahead. Shrewd businessman that he was, he'd surely have a clever trick or two up his sleeve.

She set the newspaper down on the table, gave that smiling countenance one last dirty look, then went over to the telephone to call Peggy and have her set up a committee meeting. However, before she could even pick up the receiver, it rang in her hand.

She snatched it up. 'Hello.'

'Stacey? This is Tony Devereux.'

My, how formal we are this morning! she thought angrily. Then her heart gave a little leap. Maybe he'd called to apologize, or at least to discuss the situation, both personal and business, calmly, get back on their old friendly footing.

'Oh, yes?' she said tentatively at last.

'I take it you're the official representative of the tenants' group. Is that right?'

'Well, one of them, I guess.'

'What I'd like to do is meet with you to discuss the situation.'

Which situation? she wondered, still hoping. 'Yes,' she replied cautiously. 'I think that would be a good idea.'

'Good. Say, eight o'clock this evening at my place?'

His place! She hadn't even known he *had* another place of his own. And would it be wise to go there alone? He had wielded tremendous power over her heart at one time. Should she risk it?

But before she could answer he was going on, this time in a more intimate tone. 'I just think we need to talk, Stacey. Surely two reasonable people can come to some sort of agreement about—well, about everything. I was a little harried last night, with those damned reporters dogging me, and I'm afraid I might have taken it out on you. If so, I apologize.'

'All right,' she said slowly at last. 'You realize I can't speak for my people, or make any decision on my own.'

'Of course,' he replied quickly. 'I just want to talk. If you'd rather, I can come to you, but the news-hounds are probably still lurking around the place.'

'No, that's all right. Just give me the address.' Actually, she was very curious to see where he lived.

He gave her an address on Central Park, said goodbye politely, and the line went dead in her ear.

She depressed the receiver, then stood there for a moment, thinking over this unexpected turn of events. He *must* be afraid he'd lost! Otherwise, why make this gesture? Still, it seemed he had more than business on his mind. There had been a definite personal note in his voice.

That evening Stacey stepped into the plush lobby of one of Park Avenue's most luxurious—and expensive—townhouses.

She crossed over to the desk, her footsteps echoing on the white and black tiles and resounding through the vaulted ceiling, to confront a very superior-looking man dressed in an elaborate uniform.

'Yes?' the man said, glancing up from the desk, looking her up and down with suspicious eyes.

'Stacey Sinclair to see Mr Anthony Devereux,' she announced briskly.

'Oh, yes, Miss Sinclair,' the man said, smiling and rising quickly from his chair. 'Mr Devereux is expecting you. Please, follow me.'

He led her over to a bank of elevators, where one car stood open, ushered her inside with a polite sweep of his arm, punched the button for the penthouse, then stood on the other side of the doors as they closed and the car began to rise. After a few seconds it came to an abrupt halt, and the doors slid open on to a wide foyer, also paved with black and white tiles.

There was only one door, of heavily-carved oak. Taking a deep breath, Stacey squared her shoulders, made straight for the intimidating door and rang the bell. In just a few seconds it was opened by Tony himself.

'Good evening,' he said with a polite nod. 'Please come in.'

She stepped inside another smaller foyer, then into a vast living-room, beautifully furnished and decorated in muted tones of blue and gray. A grand piano sat in one corner, beside a wall of solid glass that looked out upon a panoramic view of the city, the lights from the other buildings twinkling in the black sky.

As her eyes swept around the room it came to her that she was seeing an aspect of his life she'd never known existed. Back in the apartment building, even after she'd found out who he was, he'd still seemed merely like another tenant. Now, he might have lived on Mars for all they had in common.

'Would you care for a drink?' he said. 'A cup of coffee?'

Shaken out of her reverie, she turned slowly to face him. Here, in this setting, he was like a stranger to her. Had those arms really held her? Those lips pressed against hers?

'No,' she said quickly. 'No, thanks. I can't stay.'

He smiled. 'Well, you can at least sit down for a few minutes.' He gestured toward a long low couch in front of the fieldstone fireplace.

'All right.'

She perched uneasily on the edge of a leather-covered couch, watching him as he settled himself next to her. He lounged back easily, one arm resting on the back, his long legs stretched out before him.

'First,' he began, 'I'd like to apologize for some of the things I said last night, the way I behaved toward you.' He chuckled deep in his throat. 'I'm afraid your little newspaper ploy caught me entirely off-guard.'

'Well, as I tried to explain, it got started before I fell ill. I had no idea it would create such a furor, or that you'd be so pestered by reporters.'

'Well, I have to hand it to you,' he went on in an admiring tone. 'It was an ingenious maneuver.'

For the first time, a little ray of hope flickered within her. Maybe there *was* still a chance they could get back on their old friendly footing. At least he wasn't angry at her. In fact, he actually seemed to be congratulating her on outwitting him.

She relaxed a little more back on the couch and gave him a tentative smile. 'I'm glad you understand. Last night...'

'Oh, bother last night,' he said, with an airy wave of his hand. 'Never look back, Stacey,' he went on, moving closer to her. 'It doesn't pay—not in business, not in personal affairs. All that matters is today, the present moment.'

He was so close to her now that she could hear his steady, regular breathing, feel the rough material of his jacket through the thin silk of her shirt. Sensing that her control was rapidly slipping, she edged slightly away from him and cleared her throat loudly.

'You said on the phone that you wanted to talk to me,' she said in a voice that shook a little. 'About this condo situation, I presume.'

'Well, yes, partly,' he replied easily. 'That is, I think we need to get it settled between us, as representatives of the warring factions, before we can go on to more important matters.' He reached over and took her hand in his. 'We had a good thing going for us, Stacey,' he said softly. 'Let's not throw it away. I don't want to lose you over a mere business matter than can easily be resolved.'

Her heart melted within her. He *did* care for her! Suddenly she forgot where she was, everything that had happened. Memories came flooding back into her mind: the tender care he'd given her when she was so sick, the good times they'd had together, how just the sight of him could set her pulses racing.

His arm slid down from the back of the couch to settle around her shoulders, pulling her closer to him. She looked up into his eyes, and the desire that shone out of the blue depths almost took her breath away. His dark head came down, and she closed her eyes as his mouth claimed hers in a long, slow, sweet kiss.

Finally, he broke it off with a sigh. 'Much as I hate to end this pleasant dalliance,' he said, 'I really think we should get our business taken care of first.'

Something in his tone of voice warned her to tread cautiously. 'All right,' she agreed, running a hand over her hair and moving slightly away from him again. 'What did you have in mind?'

'First of all, I must tell you that, as clever as your publicity stunt was, it won't really achieve anything lasting in the long run.'

'Why not?' she demanded sharply.

He shrugged. 'Take my word for it. All the legality is on our side. You can keep delaying, of course, but in the end we'll win. The newspapers will lose interest after a few days and will drop the whole thing, and you'll be right back where you started, without a leg to stand on.'

As she listened to him a slow anger began to grow up inside her, that he could live in such plush surroundings, amid all this luxury, yet still deprive other people of their homes. But she was determined to hear him out to the end.

'I see,' she said tightly. 'Go on.'

'Well, what I have in mind is a compromise. That is, you call off your lawyers and their delaying tactics, and my company will do their best to find alternative housing for the tenants who can't manage the down payment for their condominiums.'

'Like me?' she said in a tight voice.

He smiled, and his hand tightened around hers. 'Actually, I had something else in mind for you.'

Something about that smile, the very tone of his voice, disturbed her, and she tugged her hand away from his. 'Such as?' she asked with a forced smile.

He shrugged. 'We can decide that later. After we get back from our trip to Vermont. For now, let's just say that I'll see to it you're well taken care of.'

A sudden chill clutched at her heart as the pieces began to click into place. The trip to Vermont. His wonderful 'compromise'. This was what he'd meant when he'd said she was important to him.

'I see,' she said icily. 'Tell me, are you going to set me up in a new apartment? Or pay for the condo? Keep me tucked away as your little bit on the side?'

A deep flush spread over his face, and she knew she'd hit a nerve. She jumped to her feet and glared down at him, her hands on her hips, eyes blazing.

'Well, I'm sorry to disappoint you, Mr Devereux,' she spat out at him. 'But I'm not for sale. If you'll remember, you tried that once before. It didn't work then, and it certainly isn't going to work now.'

With that, she whirled around and stalked out, through the beautiful room, out the massive carved door, and into the plush foyer. The elevator car was waiting. She stepped inside, jabbed fiercely at the lobby button, and the doors slid slowly shut.

Stacey's anger carried her nicely through the next several days. She was fully recuperated from her bout with flu, back at work, attending classes again, and fired with hope over the newspaper coverage of the tenants' plight. She *would* beat Tony at his own game, and, although it had begun to seem as if it might be a hollow victory, and she still had to fight down a sense of personal loss, this determination went a long way to soothe her wounded feelings.

However, she couldn't help noticing that there were no more photographers or reporters lurking around begging for interviews, and that each day the newspaper articles were shorter, until finally only the *Times* took any notice of the situation at all, and that was just a very small item, stuck back in the local news section of the bulky Sunday edition.

She sat at her kitchen table that Sunday morning, munching dejectedly on a dry piece of toast and sipping lukewarm coffee as she read the same bland two paragraphs for the tenth time. All it said was that there had been no agreement reached between the parties and speculated dubiously about the efficacy of their delaying tactics.

Finally she sighed, folded up the paper and sat, head in hands, staring out the window at the fine spring drizzle. There was no way out. She simply had to face the fact that they'd lost. Tony had been right. He'd warned her this would happen. She should have stayed that night and worked out a compromise with him.

It was too late now. She couldn't deal with him, not after that humiliating proposition he'd made her. He'd insulted her in the worst possible way, assuming he could buy his way into her bed, and after the things she'd said to him he certainly would be in no mood to negotiate with her about the apartment building.

Maybe she'd been wrong. If keeping her as his mistress was the best Tony had to offer, perhaps she should have jumped at the chance. Many women would have. She loved him, didn't she? What would have been the harm? She wouldn't have had to take money from him to have an affair with him. Wasn't half a loaf better than none?

But that was all water over the dam. She'd burned her bridges that night when she'd stalked out of his townhouse. Heaving another deep sigh, she got up from the table and went to call Peggy.

It was a glum, dispirited little group that met in Peggy's apartment that night. After half an hour of wrangling over procedure, the lawyer, Jack Gardner, finally jumped to his feet and glared around at the others.

'Can't you people get it through your heads?' he shouted. 'Stacey is right. Our newspaper campaign was a good idea. For a while even I had hopes it might work. But it's fizzled out now, and the most we can hope for is a compromise with Global.'

'But you said we could delay forever!' objected Peggy.

The lawyer threw up his hands. 'Even delay costs money. The question we have to decide is whether to keep throwing our money away on what's bound to fail in the end, or try to work something out.'

There was a lot of grumbling, but finally a vote was taken and the others reluctantly agreed. Stacey had tried to make herself inconspicuous, saying little and keeping in the background, but after the vote the lawyer turned to her.

'Well, Stacey, I guess that's it. As our representative, will you get in touch with Mr Devereux and tell him we're ready to negotiate?'

Stacey had known this was coming, but it still startled her. 'I'm sorry, Jack,' she stammered at last. 'I'm afraid I can't do that.'

She muttered something about her recent illness, and finally he agreed to tackle it himself.

Another week passed, with no news at all from Jack Gardner. Peggy had called her one afternoon at work to tell her that the lawyer had tried to see Tony, but that either he was out of town or avoiding him, and so far he hadn't been able to set up a meeting.

So now it appeared that even a compromise was no longer possible, and Stacey felt it was all her fault. She could have listened to him, even leaving aside the personal aspect of that last conversation.

Now, every evening when she came home from work, she would glance around her apartment as though it might be for the last time. What was even worse than the thought of losing her home was the emptiness of her life without Tony. She hated to admit it, but by now her anger at him had completely fizzled out, and she was fast becoming convinced that she had acted like a perfect fool throughout the whole affair.

She just couldn't seem to get him out of her mind. She kept thinking she saw him in the crowded city streets. Every time the telephone rang she felt her heart start to pound erratically, hoping it might be him, but certain it wouldn't be. Once or twice she even thought of calling him herself, but what would she say? I'm yours, on any terms? Come and get me?

One night, when she picked up her mail in the lobby, the first thing that caught her eye was another stiff envelope with the Global Enterprises logo in the corner. Her heart stood still. This was it, then, her marching papers. She'd known it was coming, but had somehow managed to keep the dreadful thought at bay, still hoping.

When she let herself into her apartment, before even taking off her coat, she ripped the envelope open. Better to read it right away and get it over with, just like the dentist. Scanning swiftly over the one short paragraph, her eyes widened. Her mouth fell open. It couldn't be! She must have read it wrong.

Slowly she walked over to the couch and sank down upon it, then read the letter again, more carefully this time.

Dear Ms Sinclair, This is to inform you that Global Enterprises has decided not to pursue its plan for the conversion of the apartment building in which you reside to condominiums. This, of course, means that the building will remain under rent-control, and the amount of your monthly rental payment will not change.

Stacey dropped the letter from her hands, laid her head back on the couch and closed her eyes. What did it mean? Why had they backed down at the very moment of victory? And whose decision was it? But before she could clear her head, and even begin to make sense of what had happened, the telephone started to ring.

It was Peggy, jubilant over what had happened, and just as puzzled as Stacey as to the reason. 'But I'm not going to argue with them, my dear,' she crowed. 'Never look a gift horse in the mouth, is my motto. Now, get yourself down here to my place. We're all going to celebrate.'

Three hours later, a bewildered—and exhausted—Stacey got off the elevator on her own floor and plodded wearily down the hall to her door. No one at the party had had a clue as to why Global had changed their minds. Jack Gardner hadn't even talked to Tony, or anyone else at the company for that matter. It didn't make any sense, but she was too tired to try to figure it out tonight.

She had reached her door by now, and was just reaching in her pocket for her keys when a slight noise across the hall startled her. Gazing anxiously into the shadows, she saw a familiar tall form come walking slowly toward her. She dropped her keys with a loud clatter and simply stood there, staring.

'Tony!' she said at last. 'Is it really you?'

His face was grave, but at her question the corners of his mouth quirked up slightly. 'Yes, it's me. The bad penny.'

'But...but...' she stammered. 'I mean, what...?'

He stooped down to pick up her keys, then handed them to her solemnly. 'I'd like to talk to you, if you have a minute.'

'Yes,' she said hastily, inserting her key in the lock. 'Of course. You'd better come in.'

He followed her inside, and when she switched on the lamp beside the couch she noticed that the letter from Global was still lying there, where she'd dropped it when Peggy called.

She saw his glance flick briefly at it, then turn to her. 'I see you received our letter.'

'Yes. Just this evening. But I don't understand...'

Then her eyes narrowed at him as the light dawned. Had he come tonight to claim his property? But, to her amazement, instead of flaring up in indignation at the thought, she was suddenly filled with a heady sense of elation. The only thing that mattered now was that he *had* come to her, was here, now, beside her.

As though he could read her mind, he held up a hand. 'I don't want you to think I did it to force you into anything,' he said hurriedly. Then he shrugged. 'In fact, I probably owe you an apology for the stupid move I made the last time we met—my offer of "assistance", to put it as delicately as possible.'

Calmer now, beginning to understand, an overpowering intuition warned Stacey just then that the less she said the better. From the strained look on his face, she knew it had cost this proud man a great deal even to come here at all, much less to apologize, and she had to let him do it his way.

'I see,' she said quietly.

He moved stiffly to the couch, and after he'd taken a seat she settled herself at the other end, her legs tucked beneath her, waiting. He sat quite still for some time, a brooding cast to his features, and as she watched him silently all Stacey could think of was how dear he was to her, how wonderful it was to be beside him again, to feel his presence, hear his voice, his breathing.

She had no idea yet what was on his mind, why he'd really come, but she did know it couldn't have been easy for him to humble himself to her in this way, and his vulnerability touched her deeply, so that it was all she could do to keep from reaching out to him, drawing him to her and cradling the dear, dark head in her arms.

Finally, he shook his head and turned to give her a wry smile. 'I'm afraid I'm not very good at this kind of thing,' he said in a low voice. 'But if you'll bear with me, I'll make a stab at it.'

He jumped to his feet then, and began pacing around the room, finally coming to a halt before her. 'Well, hell,' he said, with a helpless lift of his broad shoulders. 'There doesn't seem to be any other way but to come right out with it.' He seemed to take a deep breath before plunging ahead. 'I've missed you, Stacey. I find I can't live without you. What will it take to get you back?'

She reached out a hand to him, smiling. 'Not much,' she replied cheerfully. 'All you have to do is ask.'

A look of such intense relief passed over his face that Stacey had to stifle the sudden burst of laughter that threatened to erupt at the sight.

The next thing she knew, he'd taken her hand, drawn her up from the couch, and his arms were around her, clutching her tightly, almost like a drowning man hanging on to a life-preserver.

'Oh, darling,' he murmured in her ear. 'I was so afraid I'd lost you.'

She pulled her head back and gazed up into the glowing sapphire eyes. 'Is that why you dropped the conversion plan?'

'Well, partly.' Then he grinned. 'No, mostly. Although it won't hurt the company to take a loss this once. In fact, it might even improve our public image. But,' he added hastily, 'there are no strings. I know— I guess I always knew—you're not for sale.'

'Then, why...?'

'Why did I make that dumb proposition in the first place?' She nodded. 'At the time,' he went on carefully, 'it seemed like the only way. I never even considered that there might be an even better alternative.'

'And now?' she asked softly.

His hands were on her shoulders, the bright blue gaze boring into her. 'Now I know,' he ground out, 'that what I felt for you went far beyond simple desire. Lust, if you will.' He made a little noise deep in his throat and enfolded her in his arms once again. 'I love you, Stacey,' he murmured. 'I think I always have. Life is empty without you. I want us to be together, always. I'm asking you to marry me.'

'Oh, Tony,' she breathed, raising her arms up and throwing them around his neck. 'Of course I'll marry you. It's what I want too.'

His mouth sought hers in a passionate kiss, and she yielded herself up against his long hard body in complete abandonment. His large hands moved feverishly over her back, brushing against the sides of her breasts, then down over her waist to her hips, clutching her even closer so that she could feel his hard need pulsing against her. At the same time his mouth opened wider over hers, his tongue pressing against her lips, seeking entrance.

With a sigh, she opened herself to him, and raked her fingers up through the crisp dark hair. She gasped aloud when she felt one hand come up to settle on her breast, kneading gently, moving across from one aroused peak to the other, then slipping inside her silk blouse to fondle the bare flesh beneath.

His mouth left hers then, and travelled downward to the base of her neck, and her head fell back in a gesture of total surrender. She could feel his fingers fumbling with the buttons of her blouse, then pulling it apart, unfastening the front clasp of her lacy bra, and finally his mouth traveled lower, to nuzzle her bare breast. She clutched his head to her eagerly, cradling it in her arms as she had so often longed to do.

Then, after a few moments, she felt herself being swooped up into his arms, and as he strode down the hall to her bedroom she reached out to unbutton his shirt, reveling in the feel of the smoothness of his skin beneath it, the strong hard muscles.

At the door to her room he stopped, and gazed intently down at her. His dark hair was falling over his forehead, his brilliant blue eyes drugged now with desire, his breath coming in short bursts.

'If you want to wait until we're married, my girl,' he rasped out painfully, 'you'd better say so right now, because in just a few seconds it's going to be too late.'

For answer, she ran her open palms up the smooth chest, then bent her head to place her lips on his bare shoulder. A shudder ran through him, and in one long stride he stepped over the threshold.

When he reached the bed he set her down beside it, then slowly and methodically, as though relishing every moment, began to strip off her clothing: the silk blouse first, then the skirt, then her underwear, pulling off her tights in long, sensuous strokes, until she stood naked before him. With his eyes never leaving hers, he ran his hands down her body, from her shoulders to the soles of her feet, murmuring endearments.

'You're even more lovely than I imagined,' he said hoarsely as his hands cupped her breasts. 'Can you possibly want me a fraction as much as I want you?' he asked, with wonder in his voice.

She only smiled, then slowly reached down to his leather belt and began to unbuckle it. As her knuckles brushed against the flesh of his flat stomach he drew in a quick, grasping breath. In a frenzy now, he shrugged out of his remaining clothes, until they stood facing each other, naked and unashamed.

Then, with a low groan, he eased her down on top of the bed, hovering over her, his hair falling over his forehead, his shoulders heaving laboriously. In a moment he eased himself down beside her, and his hands and mouth began to worship her body, until finally she could bear the delicious torment no longer.

'Now, darling!' she cried out, clutching at him. 'Oh, please, now!'

He raised himself up, then slowly, deliberately, lowered himself on top of her, beginning the slow dance of love, riding the crest of the wave with her.

Some time later, Stacey raised her head up slightly off the pillow and glanced over at her lover, her future husband, her friend. When finally they had slid exhausted under the covers he'd gone instantly to sleep, cradling her in his arms, his hand resting possessively on her breast, his mouth nuzzling her shoulder.

The neon lights from the building across the street cast a dim glow into the room, hitting his face at just the right angle to illuminate it in all its masculine beauty. This man is mine now, she thought fiercely, and covered the hand on her breast with her own. In the end, she would have taken him on any terms, and he had offered her his entire life.

So, she mused happily, as she let her head sink back down on the pillow next to his, it seems as though business and love can exist side by side after all. Only this time they were playing both games for keeps. With a dreamy smile still on her lips, she closed her eyes and drifted off into a deep, dreamless sleep, lying next to the man she loved with all her heart.

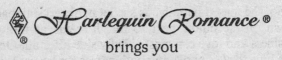
Harlequin Romance ®
brings you

How the West Was Wooed!

We've rounded up twelve of our most popular authors, and the result is a whole year of romance, Western style. Every month we'll be bringing you a spirited, independent woman whose heart is about to be lassoed by a rugged, handsome, one-hundred-percent cowboy! Watch for...

- April: **A DANGEROUS MAGIC**—Patricia Wilson

- May: **THE BADLANDS BRIDE**—Rebecca Winters

- June: **RUNAWAY WEDDING**—Ruth Jean Dale

- July: **A RANCH, A RING AND EVERYTHING**—Val Daniels

- August: **TEMPORARY TEXAN**—Heather Allison

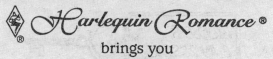

brings you

Some men are worth waiting for!

They're handsome, they're charming but, best of all, they're single! Twelve lucky women are about to discover that finding Mr. Right is not a problem—it's holding on to him.

In April the series continues with

#3406 THE RIGHT KIND OF MAN
by Jessica Hart

Skye had run away from man trouble, only to bump smack into Lorimer Kingan. He was tall, dark and handsome, and he wanted an efficient, reliable PA. Skye desperately wanted the job, but could she really describe herself as *efficient*? Worse, she knew as soon as she saw him that Lorimer was the right kind of man for her!

Hold out for Harlequin Romance's heroes in coming months...

- May: MOVING IN WITH ADAM—Jeanne Allan
- June: THE DADDY TRAP—Leigh Michaels
- July: THE BACHELOR'S WEDDING—Betty Neels

BRIDE'S BAY RESORT

UNLOCK THE DOOR TO GREAT ROMANCE AT BRIDE'S BAY RESORT

Join Harlequin's new across-the-lines series, set in an exclusive hotel on an island off the coast of South Carolina.

Seven of your favorite authors will bring you exciting stories about fascinating heroes and heroines discovering love at Bride's Bay Resort.

Look for these fabulous stories coming to a store near you beginning in January 1996.

Harlequin American Romance #613 in January
Matchmaking Baby by Cathy Gillen Thacker

Harlequin Presents #1794 in February
Indiscretions by Robyn Donald

Harlequin Intrigue #362 in March
Love and Lies by Dawn Stewardson

Harlequin Romance #3404 in April
Make Believe Engagement by Day Leclaire

Harlequin Temptation #588 in May
Stranger in the Night by Roseanne Williams

Harlequin Superromance #695 in June
Married to a Stranger by Connie Bennett

Harlequin Historicals #324 in July
Dulcie's Gift by Ruth Langan

Visit Bride's Bay Resort each month wherever Harlequin books are sold.

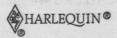

HARLEQUIN ®

BBAYG